How

To Relax

In a Busy World

HOW
TO RELAX
IN A BUSY WORLD

by Floyd Corbin

with Eve Corbin

Floyd and Eve Corbin
P.O. Box 75657, Los Angeles, California 90005

Library of Congress Catalog Card Number: 62-13196

Printed in the United States of America

43110—T

Assigned to Floyd and Eve Corbin
P. O. Box 75657, Los Angeles, Calif. 90075
In 1969

Second Revised Edition 1969
Third Revised Edition 1971
Fourth Revised Edition 1973

DEDICATION

To my wife Eve, whose loving companionship, insight and understanding, combined with her alert mind and many accomplishments have been a constant joy to me . . . I express gratitude.

To Dr. William Glassman of Encino, California, who went far beyond the call of duty by spending many hours at my bedside, employing every known medical skill to keep life flowing through me after a serious automobile accident . . . I express my appreciation.

To the many wonderful people whose love, encouragement and understanding have lighted my way . . . I give thanks.

I surround all of you with love, for each of you has had a part in making this book possible!

CONTENTS

chapter 24. **The Science of Happiness (Cont.):**

All Have a Turning Point! "To Start Your Day
Right." Our Fellow-Travelers—the Stars! Uni-
verse Stuff. How We Build Our Own Reactors.
Bon Voyage!

How

To Relax

In a Busy World

1

Danger! Tension!

In the year 1944 I awakened one June morning with a mist before my eyes. A few months later I was completely blind. In the years that followed I had to learn how to overcome the fears that come with not being able to see and to apply myself so I could act and live constructively instead of merely existing in the valley of despair.

How was I able to do this? I no longer dwell in retrospect on the steps that led me out of that valley. I seldom think of them, except in gratitude, because what I learned in the first few years of my rehabilitation has become so much a part of me that it is habitual. My reason for sharing these experiences with you is to encourage others, whatever the cause of their tensions, to deal with those causes, and not just the effects of those tensions.

My experience in learning to cope with tension brought me insight into the simple durable techniques that gave me mastery over life. As a counselor in human relations, I have shared them with countless clients beset by despair, failure and a hopeless outlook on the future. The practice of these devices has invariably reduced tension—the prime obstacle to a happy and fruitful life. Followed faithfully and with a wholehearted belief, these techniques can guide you in all human relationships. They will help you improve health, spirit and financial status. A salesman can learn from them to do a more creative selling job. The executive will learn how to deal more effectively with his staff. For the housewife, they are guideposts to family harmony. For all of us deal with the human factor every moment of the day. Not only are you deeply involved with business associates, family, but yourself. *And only when you have mastered yourself can you reach out to deal successfully with the world.* This is the key to health, harmony and success. It is the prime weapon in the never ending battle with the tensions that threaten to undo you— a battle that I have had to wage with extra vigor, for in the middle

1

of an active career, I was suddenly robbed of my vision as a result of an earlier automobile accident.

In order to understand how self mastery works, let us explore the anatomy of tension.

TENSION PERSPECTIVE

The sidewalk superintendent, who makes a hobby of watching the construction of a new skyscraper through a peephole in the fence, is filled with awe. How can the contractor assemble the variety of materials in the right place at the right time? Moreover, how did he have the knowledge and vision to submit the proper original bid, in order to earn a fair profit on the deal? To the spectator, it is all a deep mystery.

But the contractor knows the secret! He knows each segment of the project must be broken down into component parts, and finally they must all be assembled into the whole.

Now let us consider the project of reducing our tensions in a similar manner. We resolve, "This year, I shall be calm and collected." Does it work? Not that easily! We aren't emotionally equipped to handle the entire picture as one vast unit. We'll have to break down our tensions into smaller fragments. We won't even attempt to tackle the problems in a month, a week, or even a day at a time. Let's begin small—like the child who must first crawl before he can take the first steps. For we must undo old patterns of tension before we can acquire new methods of changing them. So we will make haste slowly.

But don't be impatient. This means of reducing tension can be put into practice without waste of time. The devices will fit into the spare moments of your day.

TWO KINDS OF TENSION

What does tension mean to you? Confusion, frustration, anxiety, marital and financial stress, and a general state of turmoil? You're right. These tensions are responsible for the many psychosomatic ills, human errors, misbehavior, unrest and dissatisfaction around us. These are the evils we're going to help you alleviate through simple practical procedures that have worked for us.

However, as you know, there is another concept of the word "tension." An engineer tells us, "Tension is the pressure exerted upon energy or matter to give it specific direction." Considered in this light, tension can also be a positive factor. The supervisor of a business no doubt receives his direction from the general manager. He, in turn, gets *his* direction from the president or the board of directors. Management sees to it that this "pressure that gives direction" is exerted with intelligence, foresight and ingenuity all the way down the line. Thus, each manager becomes the channel through which pressure (in the good sense of communication of goals and methods) extends from top echelon to the lowliest level. If the average worker is given clear-cut instructions and carries them out, he should derive great satisfaction from his job. Someone said, "Nothing is work—unless you'd rather be doing something else." So the realization of a job well done can take the drudgery out of a task and transform it into a source of pleasure. Work—pleasure? Sure, once the tension is gone!

For tension is the culprit. *And tension is the wrong application of energy*. Look at it this way. An experienced drill press operator will apply his drill to metal, using the precise amount of pressure. Result—success. The hole is drilled easily and without undue wear on the bit. But suppose the pressure isn't expertly applied. The hole, even if broken through, will be ragged. Trouble!

It's the same principle in driving your car. Smooth foot pressure on the accelerator gives smooth direction to the motor. The foot brake evenly applied brings the car to a gradual, effortless stop. How different from the jerky erratic driver, who is a menace to himself and traffic!

What works for the drill press and the motorcar works, in principle, for ourselves. For we react in the same way to mistreatment. How often we use our bodies carelessly! Not enough sleep, sketchy meals at irregular hours, lack of rest—these are all invitations to the deadliest kind of tension. Therefore, the simple habits of sound health are among the ingredients of our secret weapon against tension.

Man's Five Reporters

Much of man's ability to function has been developed by the correct use of his built-in circuit network. This complex system is triggered by the senses that enable him to experience his environment. This environment consists of all his contacts. These, in turn, constitute his discoveries about life. They form the basis for the decisions that govern his behavior. Let's see how information comes through to us by our five reporters.

According to science, 60 to 80 per cent of our information about our world comes to us through our eyes. We receive the remaining 20 to 40 per cent through the stimuli on the receptors of the other four senses.

Our eyes serve us in the most extraordinary way. Not only do we see an object, but we see with a kind of depth. That is, we surmise reactions through vision. For instance, it is Saturday and Johnny is on his way to play ball with the gang. You stop him. This is his morning to mow the lawn. Johnny doesn't protest. His face remains expressionless. But he throws his mitt on the floor and stalks out, slamming the door. You read resentment in his behavior, and no doubt, you deal with it accordingly. Have you ever witnessed a similar reaction in a fellow worker whom you have perhaps criticized? The shrug of his shoulder that says, "I neither like you nor your criticism, and I couldn't care less about either."

These physical acts are often more reliable indicators of feeling than the spoken word. So we become adept at interpreting the twitch of a muscle, the narrowing of lips, the gesture of a hand.

Other senses affect our lives similarly. Shake hands with a customer or a competitor and notice the difference in pressure. A handclasp is a giveaway to inner feelings—fear, anger or self confidence. You form your opinion of an individual by the conclusions you draw from the sense of touch.

Our ears also bring us information. The light nervous cough, the clearing of a throat, a shrill tone—all of them belying the pleasant spoken words. The young mother learns to differentiate between her baby's cry of need or anger. An unusual sound in your car engine alerts you to trouble. A factory foreman realizes through his trained olfactory nerves that a machine is running hot. A man is intrigued by the fragrance of perfume. Or tantalized by the aroma of hot cinnamon buns emanating from a bakery chimney. Or aroused from sleep by the smell of sizzling bacon.

We get information from our sense of taste, too. Consider those acutely endowed individuals who make a life career of wine or tea tasting.

Why are we devoting time to a discussion of our senses? Partly to become aware of their importance to our state of well being. And also to remind us that while under tension, we automatically close the door between sensing and perceiving. Our physical senses may register a stimulus. But it fails to arrive at the brain center for the processing we call "perception." If we are completely absorbed in one line of thought, we may miss up on an obvious event. Many athletes injured in action have finished the game, later to express surprise at their injuries.

We often miss those signposts along the road that would direct us to success, if only we were aware of them. Why do we miss them? Because we are so completely absorbed in another problem.

So while we gather information with our senses from many sources, it remains merely information until we digest it. Only this follow-through can bring us wisdom and understanding. This is what differentiates the wise man from the fool.

UTILIZING OUR ABILITY OF RECALL

Much of our activity is governed by our immediate reactions to our environment. However, many of our decisions are based upon past experience stored in the mental bank we call memory. We have an incredible ability to receive lasting impressions of all our experiences. Scientists tell us everything that happens to us is recorded in billions of our brain cells. It has been found that under proper stimulation, an astonishing number of events can be recalled that were not consciously observed, or were seemingly forgotten.

Hypnotism has verified this theory. In one experiment, a man was placed before a department store window. He was allowed thirty seconds to look at the contents. Then he was blindfolded and asked to enumerate as many objects as possible. By experiments with different people, it was found the number of recalls averaged eight to ten out of more than a hundred items in the window.

However, if the individual were hypnotized and asked for his recall, he scored an astonishing total, often over a hundred. These items were seen by his eyes and recorded in his brain. But under normal circumstances, many of them were forgotten. Hypnotism jogged his memory.

Now if a person is asked to repeat this experiment, day after day, he will train himself to remember more of the window contents, simply by application of his own faculties. Hypnotism won't be necessary. This kind of discipline builds character. For we grow only from the inside.

As important as a good memory is a good "forgettery." That is, to forget non-essentials. But the ability to recall on demand is priceless. Have you ever hidden an important paper so well you cannot remember its hiding place? Have you forgotten a friend's name? Have you tried to find an error in a ledger? The harder you try, the more it eludes you. Then in the midst of a completely irrelevant thought, it comes to you.

What actually happened was that success came with the release of tension.

Relaxation brought results.

Did you ever, as a child, watch a star? Did you find that if you stared long enough, it seemed to disappear? However, if you closed your eyes or looked away for a moment, the star was shining again.

This is pertinent to our daily routine. We are most effective when we are fresh. We work best when our work span is broken into segments. Tests show that after a peak of efficiency is reached, performance efficiency declines in proportion to the time spent. Hence the popularity of the coffee break.

William James discovered that the stimulation of one sense sharpens the others. Through experiments, he proved that the sound of a tuning fork near your ear not only stimulates your sense of hearing but also the other senses. This reminds me of an old cartoon. Two women were sitting in the theater as the lights dimmed. One said, "I wish they wouldn't dim those lights. I won't hear so well." Her companion replied, "I know just what you mean. I don't hear so well on the telephone when I haven't my glasses on."

Conversely, in tasting a new food, we may close our eyes to identify the flavor. Musicians often listen with closed eyes to a musical score. Blocking out one sense seems to sharpen another.

How to Sharpen One Sense

All these devices enable us to acquire maximum information through our senses. Stimulating one sense brings a wonderful feeling of relaxation. Here's a simple exercise to prove it. Read it over to get the gist of it; then follow the instructions.

Sit in a chair. Place your fingertips on your shoes. Notice how cool the leather feels, or how soft the suede. Touch your stockings. Notice the difference in texture. Now place your fingertips on your trousers (or skirt). How different this material feels! Then your belt buckle, or a button. Become aware of the contrast in surfaces. Next place your fingers on your neck. Surprisingly warm, isn't it? Touch your earlobes: they are much cooler. But the temperature of your forehead is different. Finally, place your fingers on your hair. Feel its difference, compared to your skin.

Now place your hands in your lap, palms up, but not touching. Close your eyes. Direct your mind to recall vividly the texture of shoes, stockings, trousers (or skirt), belt buckle, buttons, the warmth of your throat, the coolness of your lobes. Remember how your forehead felt, and the contrast between it and your hair. Take a deep breath. You will find yourself perfectly quiet.

Listen for sounds.

How quiet your room is! Through the open window you hear

birdsong, the hum of traffic, the sound of a barking dog. You might have missed these sounds if you hadn't made a conscious effort to become (or "to achieve") quiet. You achieved this great stillness by diverting your mind. And by stimulating your sense of touch, you stimulated all senses. Finally, you equalized your body. This served to release inner tensions.

Fun, wasn't it? Stimulating, too. Very well, let's carry the experiment a bit farther. Put a record on the player, perhaps a favorite Mozart or Beethoven. Lie back in your chair, eyes closed. Listen. Do you hear the flute repeating the statement first made by the violins? Did you ever hear it before? If you have a musical instrument, play a passage you have skipped in the past because it seemed too difficult. You will be pleasantly surprised to find how much easier it goes.

Examine the state of your mind now. Are you as tired as you were before we started? Or are you refreshed by a new flow of energy? Energy follows when tension is reduced.

The exercises in this book are all designed to eliminate the tension that blocks you from successful living. My friends helped me vanquish tension. My clients taught me how to deal with it. For as Gertrude Lawrence sang in *The King and I,* "by your pupils you'll be taught."

The weapons to fight and overcome tension are within you.

Courage is a weapon against tension.

Faith is a weapon against tension.

Meditation is a weapon against tension.

Understanding yourself is a weapon against tension.

Honesty with oneself is a weapon against tension.

The ability to put yourself in the other fellow's place is a weapon against tension.

Love stronger than self love is a weapon against tension.

Enthusiasm will free you of tension.

Standing up to your fears will free you of tension.

How to make these traits work for you, through God and Nature, is the theme of this book.

Life is yours—for the living.

When Is Tension Good?

A big game hunter was holding a group of teenagers spellbound with tales about his recent African trip. "On my last day in camp," he said, "I was following a game trail to the water hole. Suddenly I heard a noise behind me, and out of the corner of my eye I saw a huge lion stalking me. I didn't have time to shoot; he was too close! My years of experience gave me the self-control I needed to size up all the possibilities of my predicament. With a flash of perception I knew a limb offered my only chance of escape. There was one, about five feet in front of me and fifteen feet above me. 'I can never make it!' I thought. 'It's too high!' Just then the lion gave a blood-curdling roar. I sprang for the limb! But I missed it . . ."

At this point, a young doubting Thomas said, "Look, mister! If you missed that limb, how come you're here?"

"Well, you see, son," the hunter said, "I missed it on the way up, but I caught it on the way down!"

Motivation is one of the most powerful forces in the world. Motivations of fear and of love have produced miraculous feats.

In Florida, a woman, looking out of her window, saw her

Cadillac rolling back in the driveway. Her small son was in its path. It struck him, pinning his arm underneath a wheel. Although she weighed only one hundred and twenty pounds, the mother dashed out to the driveway, grabbed the bumper and lifted the corner of her forty-eight-hundred-pound car to free the boy.

A truck driver, passing an accident on the highway, saw another truck driver pinned inside his crushed cab. Gasoline had been spilled. He knew that within seconds the wreck would be enveloped in flames. Without hesitation he ran to the cab and tore the door open with his hands. Then bracing his back against the roof of the cab, he slowly straightened and raised the roof high enough to allow the injured driver to squirm out. Police, arriving a few minutes later, could hardly believe their eyes: the cab's roof had been smashed almost flat. To raise it would have taken a machine with several hundreds of pounds of pressure. Yet this man had lifted it with only his back.

We have heard of bed-ridden invalids who have dashed from their burning homes. Such instances prove there are powers within us which we do not dream we possess, since we are not called on to exert them except in cases of emergency.

A Look Over Our Shoulder

Primitive man lived on a stimulus-motivation-action basis. He existed in a state of constant alertness that enabled him to respond to the stimuli his senses reported to him. He was constantly ready to flee or to fight. If it were flight he had to decide how far it was to the nearest tree and whether he could make it. In any case, there was no time to vacillate. Self-preservation demanded action, NOW!

Trigger reactions in the physical realm led naturally to similar reactions in his human relation field. He practiced retaliation. No one knows how many generations passed before the man appeared who wanted to learn more about himself, to improve himself and to explore his universe. This desire is imbedded deep within every man, and it is responsible for all our progress. It sets man apart from the animals.

We do not know whether the first fire which man observed came from a lightning bolt or a volcanic eruption. But his discovery that fire could be used to improve his living conditions was one of his first steps upward on the energy ladder. See him there, as he squats before a heap of warm charred wood, thinking of ways he can use this strange frightening new force! The first glimmerings of the creative process!

The more he pondered upon his discovery, the more uses he found for it. Eventually he found he could heat water to produce steam which, when harnessed to machinery, would do much of his work for him. This great step revolutionized our industrial world. From it have come, in succession, our electric generators, the hydrogen bomb, atomic reactors and dozens of miracle machines that are but forerunners of the "fire power" of the future. Wrestling with ideas must have caused considerable tension in the thick skull of primitive man, but what far-reaching results have come from them! Whenever man is stimulated into expanding his awareness, he discovers ways of putting that knowledge to work. Whether this results in benefits and blessings to his family and to mankind depends on his motivation, his control of himself and his urges.

THE POWERHOUSE IN A SKULL

Let's return to our inquisitive primitive ancestor. It was he who first felt the urge to improve his relations with other men, or to gain control over them. His crude and naïve mind one day grasped the idea that in order to do so he must gain self-control. Before long he found within himself a veritable powerhouse. Once he profited by control over members of his tribe he felt before long the impulse to control other things.

He tamed wild animals and utilized their strength to work for him. He explored distant hunting grounds. He raided neighboring tribes for loot and captives. Much later, he took note of the plants he could use for food and cultivated open patches in the forest, planting seeds to produce food for his family. And at night he lay on his back on a pile of boughs and observed the stars.

Today man, continuing his search to discover himself and his abilities, bored perhaps by the humdrum, food-clothing-shelter routine of his life, is still exploring *his* distant hunting grounds. To help him now, he has books telling him of the lives of people of other times and distant lands. On his television screen he watches adventure under the sea, in the air, at home and abroad. He has at his disposal wonderful time-binding machines that make available to him the combined knowledge of past generations of thinkers and doers.

Watch him pick up one of these time-binding machines, a telescope, and peer through it at the stars and planets wheeling through space. He is amazed at this new world, and bound to think of his relation to it. Much the same way as his savage ancestor, he begins to philosophize about the incredible number of stars he knows to exist. He questions his relationship to them, and whether there can be life upon them. Musing upon his place in the vast universe, he is moved to encompass the people about him. This takes the focus of his attention from himself, and enlarges it to include all mankind.

As his vision and understanding broaden, he develops humanitarian traits: a concern over what happens to others, good will, generosity, open-mindedness and compassion . . . all traits which are far removed from the tooth-and-nail philosophy of his remote forebears. At this stage, he moves beyond the seeming limit of his five senses and draws through him, from the Great Unknown, stimuli on the receptors of other senses—senses of which he may not be consciously aware.

Many men are still wary of this type of awareness. Some dismiss it as intuition and say "That's for women!" Some have called it the sixth, seventh or eighth sense. Some call it Extra Sensory Perception. Others call it God.

"THE GREEKS HAD A WORD FOR IT . . ."

Let me give you an example of how it works. The Greeks, twenty-three hundred years ago, without the aid of mechanical instruments, by simply thinking about their universe, came to the conclusion that the atmosphere around them was not as void as it seemed. They claimed it was filled with infinitesimal particles they called "atoms," and which they described as being indivisible.

Their deductions lay dormant throughout the Dark Ages. Men did not begin to think seriously about them until thinkers like Copernicus and Galileo expounded their theories and proceeded to prove the earth was round, not flat. And they said the earth revolved around the sun, instead of the sun around the earth. When Copernicus first advanced his theory, the populace held big parties to ridicule him, walking as if they were dizzy, explaining to each other that no one could possibly stand upright on an earth that was spinning around the sun!

The advanced thinkers were so busy trying to save themselves from being burned at the stake for advancing such rash theories that they ceased to think further about what the Greeks had deduced centuries before about the atom.

THE SHADOW THAT CHANGED THE WORLD

It was not until this past century that Dalton, trying to isolate the atom for study, found himself unable to do so. However, he was able to observe the shadow of the atom as it moved through the crude smokebox he used in his experiment. This phenomenon so fired his imagination and so stimulated other scientists that they, too, "sat down and thought about and pondered" his discovery.

The result? Not only were they able to split the atom . . . In successive steps they developed the atomic bomb, the atomic-powered submarine, capable of sailing submerged for many months, atomic power plants that generate electricity, and many other peaceful uses of atomic power.

It is a good thing that we take time occasionally to trace the origins of our present scientific attainments. For it then becomes clear that the source of our attainments is the same: the springs of creative thought. These do not lie in textbooks. If our progress depended entirely on recorded and proven knowledge of the past, the future would stagnate.

Men with inquiring minds use the basic principle. They "sit

down and think about and ponder upon" a concept. This sets their creative imagination working, and out of it comes a new idea. They may try it hundreds of times before it succeeds. When it finally does, we have a satellite or an Echo balloon in orbit. If it doesn't work, they go through the same motions endlessly, until another idea comes through. There is no other possible explanation for the tremendous expansion of man's knowledge of his universe.

If we apply this principle with the same persistence to our human relation field we can in time lift ourselves to a comparable level of accomplishment. Unfortunately we lag far behind.

Thus man, a lonely little figure standing on his observation platform in space, just a pin-point in the Infinite, has discovered his ability to focus attention upon a problem and to draw through himself the knowledge to solve it. This is man's "dominion over all things," this ability by which he can produce the kind of a home, the kind of a job and the kind of a world he wants.

Alternate—for Power!

But to accomplish this a man must expand himself, expend tremendous effort, relax himself for revitalizing, and then expand himself again. He is made like a spring . . . to go into action. At rest he is coiled, potential energy: his power is latent until it is motivated and sparked into activity. He is like the spring, too, in that if either of them is held extended and tight with pressure too long, they both will lose their "snap." But there is one basic difference. The spring cannot rebuild itself when the pressure is released. If it has been stretched too far, it remains limp. But man quickly revives, is renewed and refreshed when allowed to relax so he can rebuild. Continued pressure will always exhaust him, but under pressure he loses his "snap" more quickly if he is also deluged with inharmony, frustration, anxiety, fear and feelings of guilt. The more of these negative emotions he entertains, the greater his loss of effective energy.

The way to achieve more, with a minimum of stress and strain, is by self-direction, self-discipline and an intelligent control of periods of alternating activity and relaxation. Learn to control the direction of your tension and your energy flow, alternate it with the ebb of creative relaxation, and you will release in yourself a thrilling power that can make your life a wonderful voyage into self-discovery.

3

Tensions Affect Our Health —
Cut Down Our Efficiency!

Man has always had tensions. Primitive man was in many ways more free of them than his modern counterpart. True, he had to contend with wild beasts, reptiles and all the hazards of nature and life. But there were peaceful times when he could relax. His mode of life allowed him to drain off his tensions through action and thus dissolve unneeded residue. They did not accumulate, to pile up.

When he was attacked by wild beasts or an enemy his fear gave him instant extra energy for self-protection. Today we know that in the face of danger our adrenal glands inject factors into the blood stream that increase the blood sugar level in order to give us additional strength to flee or fight.

Because early man both fought and fled, he lived to fight another day. Thus he burned up his extra energy. The average man today has scant opportunity for physical activity when he becomes angry or frightened, and therefore has little opportunity to burn up his surplus adrenalin. Society has imposed codes that make a man a coward if he runs and unsocial if he fights. What then is he to do with the tension he is still carrying?

Many persons are shocked to discover that these emotions of fear and anger have a real and potentially dangerous connection to our physical well-being, and that they are not simply a personality problem. Until very recently physicians doubted that the large vessels of the brain were capable of constricting, or if they were, it was to such a small degree that no damage to the brain could result from it.

However, three Los Angeles doctors reported to the American Medical Association convention they now have clinical proof that anger and/or fear can cause a stroke. They said the reduction of oxygen and other nutrients in the blood through such constriction can actually cause death of brain tissue. A cause of this stricture of blood vessels is adrenalin, the hormone poured out in quantity by the adrenal gland in response to extreme fear or anger. Therefore the old "count to ten" technique could conceivably be a life saver!

Early Beginnings of Tension

What is the connection between our combative and self-preservation instincts, and tension? In the animal world various species seldom attack their own kind. The great exception is in the selection and protection of a mate—then practically all males will battle each other. Perhaps in his original primitive state man never fought with his own kind either, except for this reason. However, as man began to progress and develop more gray matter he somehow came to believe it was necessary to make human sacrifices to appease the many gods he worshiped.

To supply sufficient sacrifices without recourse to members of his own family or tribe, he started raiding neighboring tribes. He believed that "to the victor went the spoils." Whenever he was successful in a raid, he carried home members of the conquered tribe. Since this bred hatred, fear and revenge among the losers, he found before long other tribes raiding his own camp in retaliation.

Soon he began to set his creative process into motion destructively, thinking about ways to overcome his enemies. He developed the blow gun and the poisoned arrow. As he progressed scientifically, he devised more efficient machines of war . . . the chariot, the tank, the bomber. Today we are the proud possessors of the missile, the rocket and the hydrogen bomb. Primitive man did *not* have the multiplicity of fears we have today!

Animals on the other hand lead a fairly placid life under normal circumstances. Even among the wild species they have solved many of the problems of individual worry. It is an inspiring sight to see a wild sheep or goat standing motionless on the highest crag, alert for danger to his herd grazing below. To certain elephants falls the task of facing to the outside of the circle formed by the herd, to watch and listen for danger while the others eat in peace. Wild geese post sentinels who guard while their fellows feed.

There are so many areas of danger in our lives today that we could not possibly cover them individually. We have placed sentinels over them as guardians of our safety. But man cannot bring himself to rely utterly on them, as do the animals. The person who has not learned self-control will fret and worry. Although this chapter is not devoted to the techniques of reducing tensions, but rather to examining them and their source, it may be well to bring in a little philosophy that has helped thousands of people deal with their tensions.

KEEPING OUR TENSIONS UP-TO-DATE

We all have a feeling of helplessness at times about the larger world problems which no doubt may account for our worrying about them. A woman approached me after one of my recent lectures and said, "I do wish my daughter-in-law could have heard you today! She has a three-months-old baby and she is just worrying herself sick over the atomic bomb. What can I tell her that will help her?"

This young mother is a good example of the type of worrier we are discussing. Someone has said "Worry is a circle of confused thoughts revolving around a center of fear." Worry is, in effect, our imagination rushing ahead of us, picturing what may happen, leaving behind our faith.

I suggested to the mother-in-law that the first thing the young mother needed was a little sound philosophy. She should examine her own beliefs in immortality. Millions of people believe in immortality, basing their conviction on the strong desire in our hearts to live forever. She needed to bolster her belief by reading and studying to gain more insight and "a reason for the faith that is in her."

Next she should realize that the laws of the universe are impersonal in their action. The law of gravity attracts one person to the earth in exactly the same way as it does his neighbor. If she were convinced that the laws governing immortality are as impersonal as those governing gravity, she must then conclude that there is immortality for all or for none. Certainly, we do not like to contemplate our own passing for any reason. But as far as our immortality is concerned, what actual difference does it make whether we die a natural death or pass on to our next experience via an atomic bomb?

To help her in a practical application of these thoughts she might use the "Alcoholics Anonymous" prayer: "Give me the serenity to accept the things I cannot change; the courage to change the things I can, and the wisdom to know the difference."

Regarding the "things I cannot change" she would soon discover that although as an individual she can do little about the threat of the atomic bomb, she *is* free to join one of the many groups over the world that are working to insure the peaceful use of the atom. Strength comes in united effort. By lending her support to such groups she would be putting her abilities to work, instead of revolving in the treadmill of futility. She would find more "courage to change the things I can" through action.

Enlarging the scope of her acquaintance, with both people and new ideas, she would be given the "wisdom to know the difference." She would then find her tensions gradually lessening. As a result she would be a better mother to her child: even infants are quick to pick up the nervous tensions of their parents. Instead of living in an atmosphere of fear, anxiety and apprehension, she would walk through every day erect, facing whatever lay ahead with strength and stability. Her baby would then develop as it has the right to do, in an atmosphere of love and security.

Is War on Your Worry List?

A word for you who may be living with the fear of a nuclear war. Remind yourself that in the entire recorded history of mankind only eight per cent of that time has seen universal peace! Ninety-two per cent of the time, since the record of man began, someone has been fighting someone! All this turmoil has inevitably affected the human race. People who lived in fear of the first flaming arrows, or of catapults, the first gunpowder, soft-nosed bullets or rockets, were doubtless as terrified as many of us are today in view of atomic and hydrogen weapons.

But as long as wars remained "rumors of war" and only threats, millions continued to build homes, farm their crops, raise families and go on about the ordinary business of living. A great many were never personally touched by war. But had they spent their days worrying about something that never came, permitting a complete disorganization and disruption of their lives, not only they would have been losers, but the world as well.

For it is the bulk of common folk who do the work of the world, and from their ranks have come much of the valuable artistic and creative expressions that have enriched our lives. Futile worry is a corrosive that saps and nullifies creative expression. We must use our sense of perspective to help us shake off our tensions, and thus relaxed, to rely on our faith!

How We Contribute to Our Own Inefficiency

In spite of our best efforts we are bound to experience physical tensions at times. Tensions severe enough to cause pain! For instance, you may decide to carry home a bag of groceries. As you set them down on the kitchen table you find your arm aches. The ache or stiffness in the muscles may prevail for two or three hours, or a day. This is the result of self-imposed strain.

Let's take another example to show how various tensions, which we apply in much the same way, affect our health and decrease our efficiency. Hold your left hand up, face high, spread the fingers wide, then clench your fist and hold it, tight. As you press down on it you will notice the knuckles beginning to turn white. Continue to put more pressure on your fist and other parts, such as the lower palm area, will begin to show white. This proves that wherever there is tension or pressure the flow of life-giving blood is inhibited. Now open up your hand and as you do, imagine how stiff your fingers would have been, had you held them tightly closed for fifteen minutes. It is evident that the act of tightening your hand muscles cut down on the flow of blood for a time, and if it lasted long enough, would have decreased the efficiency of your hand for a while, until the tension was released.

These muscles, like thousands of others in your body, are controlled by and through your voluntary nervous system: you can release and contract them at will. But imagine what happens to your heart, lungs, liver and other vital organs of your body when the muscles around them are held tight and tense for not only minutes, but sometimes for hours, days, weeks and even months, as you permit yourself to go on an "emotional binge." These muscles are controlled by the involuntary nervous system, which is affected and "triggered" by our emotions, and not by our will power. We do not relax a tense solar plexus by willing to do so. But there are things we can do to help.

There was an interesting report recently from a leading New York City neurologist, an expert on migraine headaches. There are so many ways of "curing" migraine headache, he says, that this in itself indicates we do not have a really successful treatment. Even psychiatric treatment has not been too successful. Experts are now saying the cause of this rather common ailment lies not in the physical realm, but in the personal and emotional life of the individual.

A later report from another research group claims migraine headache in the majority of cases studied appeared to be the end-result of a period of prolonged and difficult effort on an important project. Whether the project was successfully completed or not, the migraine headache made its appearance. So it would seem that the headache is an emotionally-connected by-product.

The blush of embarrassment or shame you cannot control is not limited to your face: researchers tell us it extends to every part of your body, even the internal organs. When you blanch from fear, anger or fatigue, all your blood vessels constrict. The involuntary jerk when you are startled tightens every muscle in your body, and this, too, is beyond your control.

What emotions affect our involuntary nervous system? Some of these are fear, rage, worry, jealousy, hatred, self-condemnation, a sense of guilt. These emotions have their beginnings in the mind. They convert to tension through the action of a system over which we have no conscious control, in two places in particular: the pit of the stomach and the back of the neck. The strain will make itself felt in many other areas, such as the eyes, but I found those two the most important to me.

It is my purpose to share with you the techniques that helped me when I found it necessary to start a new life. I am not a medical doctor: I do not "prescribe" these techniques for you.

But if you try them I hope they bring you as much joy and satisfaction as they have given me.

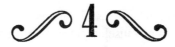

Taking the Knots Out
of the Stomach

Why is it necessary to eliminate tension in the pit of the stomach? When one is tense there, the muscles tighten down on the diaphragm. As a result, we take in only shallow breaths from the top of our lungs. The basis of the blood is iron; to purify it, one must oxidize it. To oxidize it, one must draw in sufficient oxygen to throw off the accumulating toxins which must be eliminated from the body by the respiratory system. When you breathe shallowly you do not take in the amount of oxygen needed to purify it. As a result you are likely to feel sluggish, dull and mentally fuzzy.

An Easy Way

There are many ways to alleviate this particular tension. Here is one of the simplest, which you can do almost any place. Take a deep breath. But instead of filling the upper chest, direct air to the lower part of the rib-cage . . . the diaphragm. This is the way singers breathe, using their lungs as bellows. The development of the diaphragm muscles gives them breath control. This exercise may seem hard to do at first. Try this technique. Place your hand on your diaphragm just above your waist. A man may wish to rest the bottom of his hand on the top of his belt buckle.

As you take a deep breath make your diaphragm push your hand out. (Exaggerate the motion by bringing your hand out a few inches from your body.) While you exhale imagine you are pulling your diaphragm tight against your spinal column. Press your hand against it as you do. Exhale, blowing the air through your pursed lips. Do this two or three times. Repeat several times a day. Check yourself often to see if you are permitting tension to build up in the diaphragm area: it can happen before you're aware of it!

This exercise used several times daily keeps me reasonably relaxed. It takes only a few seconds, but we must attack this problem of tension not as a whole project, but by seconds at a time throughout each day, until we develop new habit patterns.

Anyone who drives a car can practice this one without loss of time. The next time you are stopped by a red light, don't fume at the delay before it turns green. Try this: take a good deep breath, pushing out the diaphragm, then pull it back against the spine as far as you can. Hold it while you count ten. Exhale. Take another deep breath and exhale normally with a noiseless whistle.

You may find it hard to count up to ten while you hold your breath. But with a little practice you should do it with ease. The maximum benefit to your muscles is probably reached by the time you have counted to six or seven. Then you should release and contract again for the best results. I use the figure ten because it gives us that much longer to practice body control. Didn't our forefathers tell us "When angry, count to ten before you speak"? So "count to ten before you breathe." It will help you develop control not only of your body but over those nagging irritations that crop into the mind. Try erasing them during this time, and it will help prevent the accumulation of the minor tensions that add up to confusion and annoyance.

ENERGY ON DEMAND!

Most of us feel we could use more money. This next exercise is especially good for those who are burdened with "limited income" tensions. Seat yourself comfortably in a favorite chair, preferably alone. Close your eyes and picture to yourself a room filled with money. Make it as full as you wish—half full, or with money sticking out of the windows—every kind of money you can think of: $5, $10, $100 and $1,000 bills everywhere, with plenty of silver, too. This makes a real pretty picture!

Now sit up straight in your chair, feet flat on the floor and say the word "Room-full!" Get resonance into your voice and drag out the "m-m" sound until it makes your nose tingle. But before you do, start to raise your hands above your head, palms outward, and stretch the fingers as wide as you can. Then clench fists, take a deep breath, pull your arms down vigorously and stick out your chest as if to show how strong you are. Now say "ROOM-M" and simultaneously pull in your diaphragm. Then release your diaphragm and your arms as you say "FULL!" Another deep breath. Repeat the exercise twice.

This is a simple exercise, but a potent one. It not only releases tension in the diaphragm but generates a surge of energy. With it, you can revitalize yourself whenever you wish. In addition, if you want to get the maximum benefit, while you are doing the exercise, imagine yourself a good executive, salesman, hostess or whatever your role in life is. Your creative process—that is, your subconscious—will seize this combination of constructive ideas and set to work to bring them about in your life.

Is there an authentic foundation for the necessity for purifying the blood with an adequate intake of oxygen? How many of you listened to the broadcast of the Winter Olympics at Squaw Valley? Do you remember how our hockey team had beaten Russia and Holland? Then Czechoslovakia came along and had *us* beaten at the half. The Russian captain couldn't stand seeing one of their satellites doing what his team couldn't. He burst into our dressing room between halves and said excitedly to our captain, "Give the boys oxygen! They're tired! GIVE THEM OXYGEN!"

So the boys got oxygen and went out and beat Czechoslovakia in the last half. Why? The oxygen not only gave them more physical stamina and energy, but made them more alert, mentally.

MAYBE ALL YOU NEED TO DO IS BREATHE!

When this book was first published Eve and I were doing thirty minutes of breathing and stretching exercises before breakfast each morning. When Dr. Kenneth H. Cooper's book on "Aerobics" came out it made sense to us and we cut the exercises down to fifteen minutes, adding his "walk and jog" routine. We increased these gradually according to his excellent charts for our age group. Today, as the third printing of our book goes to press, we run and jog (some of it up hill) for forty minutes before breakfast.

This routine has completely changed our lives! The activity that speeds up the circulation, the deep breathing that purifies the blood, the body conditioning that results from this daily exercise . . . these make us feel thirty years younger! When *you* become a confirmed jogger, this euphoria will be yours, too. The routine will keep the weight stabilized, the muscles firm, keep the spring in the step and the cobwebs of fatigue and boredom out of the mind.

You will perform the day's tasks with vigor and enthusiasm and there'll be enough zoom at day's end to enjoy hobbies, friends and recreation. Also get Dr. Cooper's second book, "The New Aerobics" for the enlarged and improved charts.

What price good health? Perhaps the cost is the small change of perseverance, the silver of self-discipline, the gold of sincerity and the consistent payment of the promissory notes to yourself that fall due with the dawn of every new day. Only a small percentage of people see fit to take steps to keep fit. What a pity!

Speaking of breathing, — let's examine the smoking habit. I am qualified to give advice about it solely because of my experience: I smoked nearly two packs of cigarettes a day for over twenty years.

How to Stop Smoking —

The Effortless Way

(Note: If you have the earnest desire to stop smoking, do not read the techniques, pages 29-35, at one sitting. Read "Six Brass Tacks" and "The Three Techniques" one sentence at a time, and think out how each idea relates to you before reading the next sentence.)

I am not against smoking, as far as moral issues of the habit are concerned. What does concern me is the relation of smoking to health and well being; smoking as a cause and effect of tension; as an inhibitor of the type of relaxation we call "creative." I am including this chapter on smoking because of the vast number of people who, knowing its harmful effect on their health, would really like to quit, and perhaps have tried, but who thus far have not developed the control over their emotions that will permit them to quit.

No other single habit has the hold on the public that smoking does. Publicity about the injurious effect smoking has on the human system periodically flares and then subsides. But not cigarette sales or publicity. A constant stream of propaganda assails us through every publicity channel, assuring us of the joy and pleasure, not to mention the desirable social status and increased popularity with the opposite sex, which will be ours, if only we will smoke a given brand.

27

As a result, increasing millions are smoking and it is not uncommon to see children of eleven and twelve smoking as they walk home from school. Social disapproval of smoking has largely disappeared from the scene; it is now permissible to smoke almost everywhere except in church. Denominational co-educational colleges, which a couple of generations ago expelled women for smoking, now have no restrictions.

What Makes You Think You're an Exception?

We have been discussing the benefits of deep breathing. Since we depend upon the intake of air into our lungs for living, this fundamental factor affects everyone equally. Anything that interferes with the intake of fresh air into our lungs is bound to have a deleterious effect on our systems.

A group of Pennsylvania doctors made an exhaustive survey of the lung volumes of a group of men averaging 52 years of age. (They call this "vital capacity"—the amount of air a man can blow out of his lungs.) They tested all types of smokers . . . heavy, light, non-smokers and those who had stopped at least a year before. The vital capacity of *all* smokers was appreciably smaller than that of non-smokers.

Another doctor reported to an Air Pollution Conference that research had showed cigarette smoke increases the resistance to air inhaled as it passes through the air passages into the lungs, by narrowing the diameter of the air passages. He stated this narrowing is the result more of the small particles contained in the smoke than from nicotine actually inhaled. Since smoke is a necessary by-product of smoking, it makes little difference to the smoker where the blame lies for his impaired health—the smoke or the nicotine. The fact remains he is "short-winded." He is reminded in many ways that a vital part of his living machinery is operating under par.

A young man visited us one evening recently and as I brought a fresh ash tray to replace the one he had filled, he said, "I used to have an acute sense of smell but since I have been smoking so much I can't smell anything." Not only is the heavy smoker's smelling faculty diminished, but the tissues of the respiratory tract, in their effort to throw off the effect of the toxin, manufacture quantities of mucus. The coughing, spitting, throat-clearing and hawking is due to the efforts of the body to rid itself of this by-product of nicotine and harmful tars. The high incidence of colds can also be traced in part to the failure of these structures to function normally.

I wondered if our young caller had also noticed a decline in his ability to taste. We may safely assume the factors which "burn" and sting the smoker's taste buds into insensibility also weaken their sensory powers. Does this account for the insistence of many people on strong sauces and highly spiced seasonings for their food? Perhaps they must constantly stimulate their taste buds in order to experience the pleasures of eating.

The respiratory tract is lined with a fine, hair-like structure called cilia, whose function is to prevent accumulation of foreign matter on the lining. It vibrates normally at the rate of nine hundred times per second as air is inhaled. After several inhalations of tobacco smoke this rate is decreased to six hundred. It continues to decrease appreciably as smoking continues. The scientists suggest, though they have not proven it in the laboratory yet, that the impairment of this function of the cilia may permit abnormal retention of cancer-causing chemicals in the tract.

Scientists tell us, through their published surveys of experiments, that our bodies are equipped with a wonderful ability to protect us from injury provided they are allowed to function normally. When we interfere with this ability, we may expect only unhappy results.

In my files there is an imposing stack of such surveys and opinions as I have mentioned here, all by accredited and reputable doctors. If you are one of the thousands of victims of this habit I believe you will find help in this chapter.

Six "Brass Tacks"

Like countless smokers, I often made the wry joke, "Quitting is no problem! I've quit a hundred times!" Mine was the common experience of swearing off for a time, but coming back to ciga-

rettes because I couldn't withstand the smell of smoke or the craving for nicotine. When I found a simple way that helped me quit
in ten days I shared my method with many others who have also
used it successfully.

I feel better. I function better and I am happier without smoking. Only one thing is necessary for your success . . . you must
really *want* to stop!

Trying to quit smoking without some definite plan is like cast-
ing a message in a bottle upon the ocean, hoping it will arrive
on the coast of Spain. Place that bottle aboard a ship with a captain in charge, sailing orders and scientific instruments to guide
him, and we can be assured it will arrive in port on schedule.

Before I give you the three techniques that worked for me I
would like you to observe the following six preliminary steps.

1. Do not tell *anyone* that you intend to stop. This is contrary
to the school of thought which says "Tell everybody!", the idea
being you will then be ashamed not to stop. But I assure you that
telling people ahead of time will only defeat your purpose. It scat-
ters your forces. People will either sympathize with you, tease
you, or weaken your intentions by reciting their own failures to
stop.

2. Look for and recognize the excuses we feed ourselves to
rationalize our smoking so we don't have to face the actual truth.
Here are a few you will be apt to hear, when the subject of quitting comes up: "I could quit if I wanted to, but I don't want to."
"If I thought smoking was hurting me, I'd quit today, but it isn't."
"I don't drink, go to night clubs or to the movies, and smoking
is my only luxury." "My doctor told me to smoke, 'cause I'm so
nervous!" "When I quit, I gain weight, and I can't afford that!"

Ineffectual and immature people take refuge behind these
screens. They have failed to install themselves as captain of their
ship so they can arrive at their goal.

3. After you have definitely decided to quit and have set the
day for it, do not throw away your package of cigarettes. Take
them with you that day. If pressure builds up too high, take one
out, put it in your mouth *but don't light it*. After using the "success formula" I will give you later, you will want to take it out of
your mouth and return it to the package. This may sound like a

small victory, but it will give you a lot of self-confidence and a "good feeling" about the whole thing. Dispose of your package that evening. Don't carry it again.

4. Expect to be irritable during the next few days. Understand that your body had been accustomed to being whipped and stimulated by constant doses of a drug, without which it is going to be restless and uneasy. Avoid irritations and frustrating situations as much as you can. Rest as much as possible. You will get better results if your body is in the best possible condition. Fatigue drains our energy, and when we are tired we tend to be irritable. Don't eat every time you crave a smoke, but make sure your diet is right, with plenty of protein, fresh fruit and fresh vegetables. If you crave sweets or feel low in energy, try taking a spoonful of honey or a couple of protein tablets. Keep busy, either with work or play. Don't just sit, with your hands folded; find something creative for them to do.

5. Use the power of the spoken word. Your entire success may depend on the amount of feeling and emotion you put into your spoken words during this period. Remember, your subconscious is listening! It is being convinced, one way or another, by everything you say. Even if you feel uncomfortable about the wording of the "power packed" statements I am going to give you, and about repeating them, try to go along and see what they will do for you. If other ways haven't worked . . . give this one a fair trial.

6. Recognize the power of the Law of Repetition. Rely on it. In technique number 2, to follow . . . are the lines, which, if properly used, will help you accomplish your goal: to quit smoking! Say those lines aloud whenever you can. Memorize them so you can repeat them to yourself wherever you are. Or write them down on a little card and carry it in your wallet or handbag. Every time you open it, read it! Reading or hearing ideas repeated impresses them deeply on all levels of the mind. This principle underlies all advertising and is the one the cigarette companies have used so effectively. You have heard the line about the wonderful "clean, fresh taste" and invigorating effects of smoking so often you are almost convinced against the evidence of your senses that it is true! I suggest you use the same principle

to convince your subconscious mind of your power over the habit, of your mastery over yourself.

Some people suggest the best and least painful way to break a strong habit is to do it gradually. This reminds me of the Dutchman who decided to crop his little dog's tail, and hating to hurt him, cut it off an inch at a time! I am indebted to Mr. A. Nonymous, for the following thoughts on habit.

> Habit is so strong, it cannot
> be broken piecemeal. For . . .
>
> If you cut off the H . . .
>   You still have A BIT.
>
> Cut off the A . . .
>   You still have a BIT.
>
> Cut off the B . . .
>   You still have IT!
>
> Cut off the I . . .
>   You still have half of IT!

Because the smoking habit is deep-rooted and powerful, you should not be ashamed to seek spiritual help in eradicating it. You may have found in the past that your own efforts, unaided by recourse to your deeper spiritual resources, have been unequal to the job of divorcing yourself from cigarettes. This time do not hesitate to turn for help to the Power within you, the Power that created and sustains you.

Every person has his own concept of Deity. Turn to yours in any form of prayer, treatment or contact that "feels right" to you. Establish a communication both natural and spontaneous. There is Something that operates in every one of us. Why not turn to the Maker of the laws upon which the universe is based, for help? I like to use the word "Father" because this brings me very close to the Divine Intelligence I know is within me. It is my name for the friendly, cooperative Helper I can always rely upon.

1. UTILIZE THE LAW OF IMAGINATION

You have been thinking about quitting smoking. The next time you toy with the idea, enlarge upon it. Imagine how much better you are going to feel after you have stopped smoking. See yourself, completely free of the habit, refusing a cigarette easily and without strain when one is offered you. Hear yourself saying, "No, thank you, I don't use them." Repeat these simple words, as you would practice your lines for a play. Imagination is one of the most potent forces in the world. Make it work for you. Let it set the stage for the first act of your own play, entitled "How I stopped smoking!" You are the leading actor in this play, the supporting characters are the people around you who come and go, furnishing your cues. Since nothing outside of yourself has more power over you than your own feelings, you can say "No!" with sincerity and conviction.

Repeated imaging of yourself in the role of master over your own actions will build up a certain momentum within you. After the mind long pictures a scene, we get the impulse to "act it out." When this comes to you, get into action! Produce your play in real life! Some morning you will get up feeling "This is the day!" Acting at the peak of this crest of feeling will carry you to victory.

About the time you used to reach for the first cigarette, do something to carry you through that moment. Make yourself do some exercises. Take a walk. It should be something strenuous enough to absorb both your mental and physical energies and attention.

Here is one of my favorite exercises during this preliminary period: lie on your back on the floor, so that your knees are flexed and your toes extend under the edge of a davenport or large chair. Now, without using your arms or elbows to aid you, raise yourself to a sitting position, then slowly lower yourself to the floor. If you are in good condition and used to exercise you may be able to do this five times without tiring. If not, do it two or three times, then stop. Rest by extending your arms over your head while your body is still flat on the floor and inhale deeply two or three times. Repeat the exercise. In a few days you should be able to work up to ten times or more. Incidentally, this is an excellent way to strengthen the midriff and back muscles and streamline the waist. Before you get up, plan what you are going to do. Keep so busy you won't have time to reach for that cigarette.

2. UTILIZE THE LAW OF REVERSABILITY. We use this to reverse a habit pattern. You CAN change your attitude of "I want a cigarette" to its opposite "THERE IS NOTHING WITHIN ME THAT DESIRES TO SMOKE." Your body, in itself, is just a collection of molecules, flesh and bone, without the power of conscious thought. *All desire is born of the mind and spirit of man.* You CAN control your mind, if you wish to. Make the Law of Reversability work for you!

3. UTILIZE THE LAW OF REPETITION. When you feel the urge to smoke, say to yourself, "THERE IS NOTHING WITHIN ME THAT DESIRES TO SMOKE." Repeat this every time the desire enters your mind. Actually, we are learning how to use three Universal Laws to help us attain a goal. No one breaks a Universal Law: it remains the same, no matter how many people dash themselves against it. The Law of gravity is not broken because you fall and hurt yourself! The Law of mathematics is not broken, because you offer the wrong answer to a problem! Mature people learn to work *with* the Law and how to make it work for them.

Advertising firms know the value of visual repetition! They know you are influenced by the cigarette ads along the highways and in the magazines. Apply this principle for your project! Write "THERE IS NOTHING WITHIN ME THAT DESIRES TO SMOKE" on cards and put them on the bathroom mirror . . . over the light switches. Old stuff, you say? Sure, but it works! As you progress be aware of each small victory: over an hour, a day, a week! Be grateful for your ability to stop smoking.

Personally, I like to use a "treatment" or little prayer, aloud if possible: "Father, I am grateful for control over my emotions that makes it possible for me to say with sincerity and conviction:

"This is the year my desire comes true
For the Father and I are one, not two,
For I have stopped smoking the effortless way
Because I have chosen to do it this way.
This is the answer, this is the "How"
That makes me free and self-controlled now.
Thank You, God, for my desire coming true
That You and I are one, not two!"

Is It Worth It?

What are some of the benefits of not smoking? One of the finest is the certainty that you are allowing your body to regain its normal chemical and physiological harmony. You have the satisfaction of knowing that *because you chose* to eliminate an injurious substance that was detrimental to your health, you will enjoy a better functioning body.

We feel it a privilege to have known the late Dr. Walter Russell and his lovely wife, Lao and the fine work they have done through their University of Science and Philosophy at Waynesboro, Virginia. In her challenging book, "God Will Work WITH You But Not FOR You" Lao has an interesting approach to this idea of body harmony. She says:

"Every creating body forever repeats the pattern of its beginning . . . After millions of years of repeated unfoldings the various patterns thus developed . . . give to creation the types and species with which we are familiar. The seed pattern constantly changes because it is constantly added to. All bodies must unfold in harmony with their patterns. They cannot do otherwise. Each pattern has a chemical formula which has become necessary to produce that particular type of body. That formula for man includes many elements such as iron, calcium, iodine, nitrogen and oxygen.

"Any other elements than those included in the man-formula, and in the proportions required to continue life, immediately reverse the life process to the death process in small or large measure, if those added elements are out of harmony with those required by man. If any element is taken into the body which is not harmonious to that formula it injures the body. We call it a poison. A little poison can be thrown off by the body but a large amount of it will kill, slowly or quickly according to the dose.

"Nicotine is a chemical formula which does not belong to the chemical formula which has been registered in the seed of man for millions of years. A spoonful of nicotine would kill a man immediately if taken at once. A very minute dose of it does not kill him immediately but it begins to kill him over a long period of time. Even one cigarette starts the death process. Even one cigarette or cigar begins to change the man-body chemical formula to another formula.

"The new formula unbalances the normal one to such an extent that tensions develop and increase until they become permanent in any smoker's life. That means that never again, after nicotine has become a necessity, can any smoker fulfill the first law of Nature which is to so completely balance every transaction of his life that all tensions are canceled at the end of every pulsation. That foreign element which does not belong to the man-body formula prevents that cancellation. Its tensions cannot be voided. Complete rest and relaxation become impossible for the one so addicted to it that he is enslaved by it.

"A man who is deeply worried cannot relax and sleep soundly, for he is unable to cancel out his tensions. The nicotine addict carries those tensions into his sleep, into his business and even into his nourishment. The tensions of his cravings awaken him in the night. He must now add more nicotine to balance his new self-made formula. He reaches for a cigarette, perhaps another before he can sleep. He is nicotine hungry! Likewise he reaches for more cigarettes while at work in his office because he is unable to think clearly until he has satisfied the demands of the new kind of body and the new kind of hunger he has created for himself.

"Toxins and tensions begin to multiply within a man's body from the moment he begins to change the normal chemical formula which kept his metabolism in a balanced condition."

I did not come upon this passage from Mrs. Russell's book until shortly before I started writing this chapter. But it seems to me to contain truths regarding the chemical imbalance caused by the intake of nicotine into the body that I thought would be of interest to you.

If you want a demonstration of the stress caused the heart muscle by smoking, ask a doctor to try the following experiment with you. Sit quietly in his office for a few minutes, with no exertion, emotion or conversation. Have him listen to your heart through his stethoscope and note the rate. Now light up a cigarette and inhale deeply, with the stethoscope still in place. Ask him to listen for any change in the rate. Now another inhalation, and another. At the end of the third inhalation ask him to write down the rate of the heart beat. Don't be surprised if your heart beat rate has increased by thirty per cent or more. This is average, and will hold true whether a cigarette, cigar or pipe is smoked.

Everything in the system must be speeded up to compensate for this increase. Blood must circulate faster; breathing must be stepped up to furnish the blood that much more oxygen. This cycle is repeated until eventually we arrive at the point that each puff is like applying a whip to a tired horse. At work, when our performance graph starts toboganning from fatigue or hunger, instead of furnishing the body with fuel for energy, we have another cigarette. No wonder those who break their night's fast with a cup of coffee and a cigarette instead of a good breakfast are nervous and jittery by 10:00 A.M.!

These techniques have worked for me. I consumed two packs a day for over twenty years. Yet I have never even desired to smoke since the day I quit, some twelve years ago now. Naturally I do not attribute the good health I enjoy entirely to abstention. I do feel better in many ways, but this addition has given me the satisfaction of knowing I have control over myself.

I believe that if you really want to quit smoking, you can. By the power of the Imagination, the power of the Law of Repetition and the power of the Law of Gratitude.

Success, long life and happy, smoke-less days!

Addendum

(Since the first printing of this book in 1962 results of the survey by the Health, Education and Welfare Department were released by the Surgeon-General's office, substantiating the fact that smoking is a contributing factor to the incidence of lung cancer, heart and circulatory diseases, etc.)

Taking the Kinks Out of Your Neck

Emotions that move out from the brain to the far reaches of the body tighten us in two places in particular—the pit of the stomach and the back of the neck. If we can train ourselves to observe the causes of this tension, we can often avoid it.

When you become irked at someone, you are likely to feel pressure and tension in the back of the neck. How often we hear the phrase, "That person is a pain in the neck!" It is true that irritation and resentment, if strong enough, will tighten your neck muscles to give you actual pain, as severe as if there were a physical cause.

This type of tension may also develop because of fear. For example, we may be called upon to speak unexpectedly before an audience. The body will react with symptoms of fear: palpitations, faster breathing, flushes, trembling and perspiration, and a lot of tension in the back of the neck and head. A new situation, a job in which we feel incompetent or where there are too many details to master immediately can cause this muscle tightness. And when we do an unaccustomed task, such as typing or sewing, for a time, we really tighten up!

We do not realize the strain of being in an unfamiliar environment, such as a downtown shopping expedition. Though no fear or anxiety is involved, the crowds, traffic, the intensity of thought and necessity of making decisions, call for an unusual expenditure of energy, which results in fatigue. Neck and shoulder muscles begin to ache from tension.

In this condition we are not capable of expressing our best personality. Efficiency is at low ebb. If we happen to be in a supervisory capacity we will not have the alertness necessary to deal with employees and customers.

What can we do about these physical tensions? Why is it so necessary to alleviate them?

In a person of average weight, the heart pumps approximately forty-two hundred gallons of blood through the body every twenty-four hours. A gallon of this amount goes to the head area every minute.

We have heard of cases where a person injured in an accident with the blood shut off from the brain for two or three minutes, never regained his normal regimen of consciousness. Nor did some parts of his body function normally again. The important nerve centers of the brain that send out impulses to the entire body demand an adequate supply of oxygen and other life-giving factors carried by the blood stream. Tension through the neck and shoulder area has *the effect* of shutting off the blood supply to the upper area. Science is leaning toward the theory that there may be actual constricting of the blood vessels. Here are a few simple ways of loosening these tight muscles.

SOME SIMPLE TENSION-EASERS

Whenever my neck and shoulders tightened I massaged the back of the neck and skull with my finger tips. Invariably I found some sore spots. After a few minutes' rubbing they commenced to loosen. I would turn my attention away for a few minutes, then massage again. Before long the tense spots would completely disappear. I also found sore spots on the sides of my neck, throat and Adam's apple responded to massage; likewise the forehead and temples. I got a bonus, too! Massaging the head area alleviated the frown lines around my eyes.

Several years after my discovery I read a report of the experiment by one of the Eastern colleges on people suffering from insomnia. They discovered these patients to be tense at the forehead and temples. As this localized tension was eased the patients began to sleep better. I have heard it takes seventy-four muscles to frown but only fourteen to smile! A person with a smile is younger-looking and he grows older more mellowly than one who scowls! This may be the meaning behind the saying "A young woman has the face she was born with, while on older woman has the face she has earned!"

Another good technique I learned early in my readjustment was going through the motions of writing positive words such as Love, Joy, Health, Peace, Poise, with my nose! This is an excellent way to loosen up neck, head and shoulder muscles. Even more important than the physical aspect is the great mental relaxation that comes with memory and imagination.

Let's take the word "JOY." Remember how the longhand J looks? Then the big round O and the letter Y? Here's what you do: imagine your nose about six inches longer than it is. Sit up straight with your head in perfect balance and aligned with your spine. Eyes closed, actually trace the word "JOY" with your nose. Start by turning your nose toward your left shoulder; then move the nose toward the ceiling for the top part of the J. Now bring the nose down toward the floor, and back up to your shoulder to complete the bottom half of the J. Let your head slip to the center, and with your eyes still closed, take a deep breath.

Exhale, and turn your nose straight up to the ceiling and begin the round letter O by bringing your nose down the left side toward the floor, letting your chin come across your chest, then bring the nose up around the right side to the ceiling again. Release the head and take another breath.

Turn the nose to the right shoulder and up toward the ceiling write the little yoke of the top part of the Y; bring your nose down toward the floor and put the tail on the Y by taking your nose back over your right shoulder. Finally, let your head slip to the center again, and open your eyes.

Did you notice during this time that you had forgotten all worries and troubles you had when you started this relaxation drill?

What happened to them?

Simply this: you put your attention, or mental focus, on the picture of the word "JOY," which completely absorbed your conscious mind in the process. The moment you did this, your subconscious mind was permitted to take over and normalize your body which no longer was being disturbed with worries, anxieties and inner tensions. It is surprising how well we function; how our subconscious mind knows to make our heart beat, to make us breathe the proper number of times per minute, and to make the rest of our complicated mechanism perform. By getting our "bloated nothingness out of the way," as Emerson said, we help our autonomic nervous system to function as it should. Tensions are released and a feeling of well-being begins to creep in.

My first experience with this nose-writing technique came in a class on Eye Education under the instruction of Margaret Darst Corbett in Los Angeles. Valuable suggestions on relaxation appear in Mrs. Corbett's excellent book, *Help Yourself to Better Sight,* published by Prentice-Hall, Inc. My technique varies from hers, as yours will vary with use. But the principle is the same. As you do this simple relaxation, notice how rested you feel. You may even take a deep sigh as you do it—evidence of your complete relaxation. Mrs. Corbett suggests you do not make a neck exercise of this or it loses its value as eye relaxation.

Your investment is small . . . only two minutes of time. But it will help you develop the habit of letting loose. Do it night and morning: you'll sleep better, your mind will be clear in the morning.

People have told me they have been able to reduce their blood pressure several degrees by consistently doing this "nose-writing." I am a strong believer in variety—it keeps us from getting stale. Try a couple of variations of this exercise.

Sitting comfortably, place your palms and fingers together in the prayer position, holding them about six inches before your face, slightly higher than the eyes. With your eyes closed, turn your nose up toward the tip of your fingers. In your mind's eye, use your nose to draw a white line from the tip of your fingers down the right arm to your elbow. Then another straight line from your right elbow across to the left; then up the left arm to the finger tips. Try to "see" your hands and arms as you do this.

To vary it still more: as you draw the white line from the tip of the left elbow to the tip of the fingers, inhale and extend your chin. As you come down the right arm, exhale and retract the chin. Hold your breath as you draw the white line across to the other elbow. Inhale again and draw the line up to the finger tips. You may find yourself yawning and wanting to stretch all over as you do this, which shows you are really "letting down." There is something in this rhythmic, deliberate breathing that has a calming and comforting effect.

Now for the shoulders, shrug them forward, stick out the chest and pull in the diaphragm. Lift the right shoulder high and rotate it as far as you can, 'round and 'round. Then the left. Now pull them both back and let them drop comfortably.

A WORD TO THE WISE (*Who Have Kinks in Their Neck*)

Remember to check neck and shoulder muscles for tension, several times a day!

Find a sore spot? Rub it away.

Neck stiff? Write the word "LOOSE" with your nose whenever you can.

When you invest in yourself you can't lose.

Some very popular treatments for tension come in bottles.

But you'll be ahead if you use your head both to prevent and reduce your tensions!

Freeing the Mind from Tensions

Troubles are like the eggs under a setting hen. If we get off from them long enough, they won't hatch!

While on an emotional treadmill, we are like the little dog chasing his tail but never catching it. After a while the dog tires of his fruitless chase and lies down to rest. But we have more stamina! We can keep going, day after day, week after week with nothing more to show for our efforts than emotional involvement to trigger still more stress and strain.

Our mental processes at such times are largely emotional reactions. Very little actual reasoning goes on. We seem to have no constructive goal and almost seem to enjoy "stewing in our own juice." We are miserable but haven't the desire or the know-how to extricate ourselves from the cycle. As I told you earlier, worry is a circle of confused thoughts revolving around a center of fear. Fear or apprehension no doubt furnished the seed for our present crop of worry. Anxiety and uncertainty account for our confusion and indecision. This is the reason for our "fuzzy" thinking, those periods when everything seems to go wrong for us, and we make hard work of every task.

WARP AND WOOF

It is almost impossible to separate techniques for attaining mental relaxation from those for physical relaxation. The physical and mental constitute the warp and the woof of our daily lives and upon them we weave the fabric of our individual patterns. What affects one will certainly affect the other. The body will reflect the tension of the mind by exhibiting unnecessary stress. A tense muscle is an active muscle and when a muscle is active for no good reason, i.e., the accomplishment of some specific purpose, that tension is unnecessary and therefore wasted.

The person who worries after going to bed may find he is holding the weight of his head up from the pillow slightly, forcing his neck muscles to work needlessly. The person who taps his fingers, bobs his crossed foot, and constantly adjusts his clothing is reflecting his mental strain through his body gestures. Every muscle action is a proportionate drain on our physical energy!

Years ago when I did considerable counseling, I had a copper planter filled with ivy hung over my desk. When a client suffering with anxiety came in I often said, "Have you noticed this beautiful planter? The ivy looks real, doesn't it? But it isn't." Then I would add, "Now, did you notice that during the time we talked about the ivy you had completely forgotten about yourself?"

This temporary diversion is a help, but it is not a cure-all for our tension. It is simply one of the many small devices we can use, to give the mind a chance to regain its balance and poise. We can actually think of only one thing at a time. When I needed to find quiet within myself, I found these little techniques also brought me increased vitality, clarity of thought and self-confidence.

"MADAM, WILL YOU WALK?"

Walking is an excellent means of relaxation. Combine it with an enjoyment of Nature and you have a combination hard to beat. On a walk around the block, see how many different colors you can spot. Then go home and write down what you have seen. A third-grader will say "I saw a red rose"; how much more vividly can you say it?

For the next week's project, notice all the scents on a walk around your own block; then write a description of them. Listen for all the sounds, on another lap around the block, and itemize them on your return home.

Walking is a part of our own routine of living. No matter how late we come in at night, we take our walk. It seems to rid us of any surplus mental energies stored up during an active evening, and we sleep better for it. We do several laps around the park in the mornings. We sing the first verse of "Oh, what a beautiful morning!" from *Oklahoma!* and mean it. To breathe deeply and to improve our breath control, we choose a favorite hymn and give it our personal "treatment." We take a long breath and sing the first line, holding the last syllable as long as possible. Another long breath, exhaling by blowing the air through the mouth. Then the long breath for the second line, and so on. Some physical culture teachers advocate counting to five as you inhale, and to fifteen as you exhale. At first this may seem a long time, but we are counting to 25 now, so we have made progress—our "vital capacity" has increased! Next time you feel tired in the evening, instead of taking a nap before dinner, or a cocktail, try a brisk walk, breathing deeply and singing or humming softly. See how quickly that old tired feeling disappears. Think about nothing except how much you are enjoying yourself. Swing your arms freely. Relax. Make it a daily habit.

Prelude to Relaxation

We need to get quiet once a day and preferably twice, in order to dissolve the day's residue of tension. One quieting technique is the "Rose Meditation." If possible have someone read the meditation to you; you will soon learn to take the mental journey by yourself and find that in a matter of minutes it clears your mind and restores your energy.

There is something particularly healing about the beauty of

Nature. Fishermen and hunters are seldom primarily interested in fish or game they bring home. They go for the peace and relaxation to be found in the midst of Nature. The amateur gardener seldom works for the price of the flowers or vegetables he raises: he digs for the joy and relaxation of being close to Nature.

In our busy city lives we can't run off to the country or out to the garden whenever tension strikes. But we can go into our closet, so to speak, close the door and find quiet by diverting our attention to the colors and beauty of Nature.

If you want to "shape your destiny" and direct your future activities in some specific way, an excellent time to do this is at the end of the "Rose Meditation," when you are completely relaxed. Give yourself a little auto-suggestion. The subconscious mind is at this time particularly amenable to constructive thoughts. Always repeat your own name at the beginning of the "treatment" as I do in the example I give you. Work out your own terminology in a form easy and natural for you.

Get comfortable. Sit upright and easy, but don't slump. Stretch your legs out in front of you, lifting your feet off the floor; stretch the toes out, then the heels and move them about until they feel good, then return them to the floor. Take a deep breath. Lift your arms above your head, spread the fingers wide and move them about. Clench the fists and shove them toward the ceiling, then drop them in your lap, palms up, fingers relaxed but not touching. Take a deep breath, lean back in your chair and close your eyes. If no one is reading this to you, let your imagination help paint the picture in your mind's eye.

THE ROSE MEDITATION

Imagine that you are stepping out the side door of a palatial home on the lawn. As a child, if you loved the feel of warm grass under your feet, just mentally slip off your shoes and walk across the lawn to a deck chair. It is a bright stainless steel chair, with yellow upholstery, facing north. It is high noon, a beautiful day without a cloud in the sky. As you sit down in the chair you feel the sun warm on your head, back and shoulders. There is a little breeze stirring. Now, in your mind's eye, with your eyes still closed, look out in front of you and there is a freshly washed sidewalk; see how clean, cool and inviting it looks! See how green the grass is on the left side of the walk, and compare it with the white sidewalk; now look at the green grass on the right side. Then follow the walk until you come to a bed of roses, red, yellow and white.

In our mind's eye, let's go and pick up that big red rose over there. Smell the fragrance of it. How perfectly every petal is placed, the same distance from the center to each side. It is perfect as Nature would like to have all of us. Near it is a bud as big as your thumb, and the red is beginning to break through the green husk. Next to it is a tea rose in full bloom; as you look at the blending of the red and the yellow in its petals, you wonder how Nature could ever have produced anything so lovely. It, too, has a bud, about the size of an egg, that will soon be in full bloom. Over to your right is a white rose, the biggest one you have ever seen. It has a bud about the size of your little finger, and there is a speck of white petal beginning to peek through the green husk. Look at the contrast between the little speck of pure white, the light green husk and the black earth.

Now follow the walk to twin palm trees; they are the fern type palm, one on each side of the walk. Their brown trunks have been trimmed to look like two huge pineapples; their green fronds hang over them like huge umbrellas. There is a little clump of violets! See how purple the little flowers are, how straight the stems! And what a contrast between the deep purple of the blooms and the dark, veined leaves!

Follow the walk to the foothills. There are houses, white houses with red roofs, with green roofs, and living in them are men and women just like you and me. They have been brought up under different conditions, but deep within them is the little Voice telling them when to eat, when to sleep and what to do, if they will but listen to it.

Directly behind the foothills is a majestic green mountain range. At its peak is a little bank of snow, sparkling white in the noonday sun. Do you see it? Directly behind the peak is the most beautiful blue sky you have ever seen, a robin's-egg blue.

It is peaceful, lovely, and still. As you associate the beauty and quietness out there with the quietness and peace within, you begin to notice how quiet it is about you—first, five feet to the left, then ten, then fifteen; then on the right, five feet, ten and fifteen; in front of you and in back of you.

Suddenly it comes to you that regardless of what happens in your daily activities there will always be as much sunshine as you can absorb, as much fresh air as you can breathe, as much beauty as you can appreciate and as much love as you can accept. Then, going back out into the blue sky for millions upon millions of miles and feeling the warm sun on your head, back and shoulders, you begin to let down; you begin to let loose; you begin to let God take over. You know that deep within you is the place where you can always turn and become calm, quiet and collected. As you do this, you can return to your daily activities, always expressing the best within you until it comes to full expression.

While you have this picture still in mind, let's go back out into that blue sky again, then drop down to the little bank of snow on the mountain peak, then down to the houses with their various colored roofs, to the palm trees, the clump of violets, the rose bed, the white sidewalk and you. You realize there is an Infinite Intelligence moving through all things: It knows how to heal the bark on the palm tree when it becomes scuffed: It knows how to turn the sunflower to the east in the morning: It knows how to heal the cut on our finger, and It knows how to guide and direct us if we do not allow tension to block Its operation.

Let go of the tension in your body now. First, release it in all your toes, then in the bottom of the feet and ankles, and just let the floor hold them up. Loosen the muscles in the calves of your legs, the knees, thighs and hips, and feel the warm blood rushing in to heal and vitalize them. Let go of the tension up and down the spine, first on the right side all the way up to the shoulder, then down the left side, and around to the diaphragm. Release all the tightness in and around the heart area, the lungs and shoulders. Let your hands go completely limp, loosening the fingers, palms and wrists. (Appreciate your hands, for through them you express your own individuality; through them you serve; through them you express love, beauty and kindness and all the skills that have made you a good human being.)

Next release all the tension in the forearms, the elbows, the biceps, the shoulders, the back of your neck and head, and then in the throat, chin, mouth, lips and nose. Finally, smooth out all the tightness around your eyes and in your forehead.

Now in this same way let loose every fear, worry and anxiety of the past—every bit of hatred, jealousy, anger, self-pity, resentment and envy. To take their place let's establish a new mental attitude of joy—of health and happiness, of peace of mind, prosperity, and abundance of all good things.

Now you are ready to share this attitude. "Blessing" is a good word: it means wishing someone well. Think of the people to the left of you, in this room, this building, near or far, and bless them and hope that they too are enjoying or that they will find for themselves, all these good things. Now the people on your right, near and far, the people behind you, in front of you. Finally, bless everyone in your community, your city, your county, state, nation and the world.

This is the time to shape your destiny by saying mentally or verbally: "I (repeat your name), take time to do the important things to improve my self-control and efficiency, as a person. I take time to be quiet and to read. I take time to give my body the exercise it needs to keep me well. I take time to clear my mind of resentment and hatred each day, so no residue remains when I go to sleep. I take time to be friendly and to express good will and love to every person I meet. I take time to laugh and be joyful—it is healing for my soul. I take time to work so that I can become successful.

"I take time to unwind before I wind up, so I can operate more efficiently. I approach all problems as challenges that I can meet successfully. I am grateful for all the good things of life that are mine."

Take a deep breath and blow it out through your mouth. Another one. Now turn your nose straight up to the ceiling and write the letter O, coming around to the left slow and easy, letting your chin come down on your chest, and trace the O back up the right side all the way to the top. Release it and take another breath. Open your eyes. See how rested you feel! Tailor this whole technique to fit your needs. Practice it until it becomes a habit.

It can bring you more poise, peace and well-being than anything you have ever experienced.

Don't Jam the Computers
of Your Mind with Tensions!

Have you ever tried to think of a person's name and couldn't? The harder you tried, the more elusive it seemed. Then you thought of other things, and suddenly, the name flashed in your mind.

How often have you searched in vain for an error in your bookkeeping or your check stubs, only to give up in disgust? You said "To heck with it!" and went to the drinking fountain, or took a walk; on your return to your figures, you found the mistake immediately.

There seems to be some factor in our minds, possibly a different level than our conscious mind, that often works best without direct attention. Like a shy child, it will not perform "for company" but turns in a fine performance when left alone for a while.

This is why the technique of diverting our attention from our problems for a time is so valuable. Biographies of famous men are filled with examples of inspirations that came when they were least expected. Symphony themes, plots for famous novels, breakthroughs in the scientific field . . . all have appeared in the most irrelevant circumstances, sometimes suddenly and wholly unexpectedly.

Does this mean we can sit back and expect these moments of inspiration without a background of preparation? Far from it. They will not drop like manna from heaven into our hands. We need, in fact, to do considerable "pot-boiling" before these flashes of insight appear. They are brought to us by the part of our minds I call "the creative process." This is not to be confused with the "computers of the mind" that we will discuss a little later. You must consciously give your creative process fuel to work with.

The Watched Pot

For material, it needs facts and information. If you are starting a serious project, muster all information available. Read books on the subject, write to experts for their opinions, gather statistics, talk to people in the same line. . . . This body of facts is the material your creative process must have to work with. The more accurate and complete it is, the better results you will get.

The fuel that makes the "pot boil" is the energy you pour into your project and the depth of your desire to accomplish it. Remember that "Power flows to the focus of attention" and that "Man's destiny is determined by his desire for expression." It is only after you have conscientiously presented your creative process with fuel and material but still do not have your answers, that you can safely leave it to simmer. If you watch it, it won't boil. If you sprinkle it with worry, constantly stir it with tension or beat it with force, it will not produce for you. Look at something else or take a snooze, and the simmering period will often be productive. Your creative process has another ability: it can take two or three ideas, put them together and come up with a fresh idea only remotely related to the others but superior to all of them. It has an incredible synergistic power. That is why "brain-storming" sessions are often productive, although here many creative processes are at work.

THE CARE AND FEEDING OF MENTAL COMPUTERS

Now to get back to our "computers of our mind." They give us different kinds of answers and are an extremely important part of our equipment as human beings. The action of our mental computers is based on all our past experience, observation, training and innate abilities. They react almost instantly to each situation, using these factors plus all available pertinent material bearing on each situation, to enable us to act with good judgment and dispatch.

For example, your computers govern your decision as to how hard to hit a pitched ball—certainly with little time to ponder the matter. They help you gauge the distance of your car from the exact spot where you want to stop, and how much pressure to apply to the brakes. Drawing on your experience, you know almost exactly how long it will take Jones, at the office, to get that survey out. The cook who used to put in a "pinch of this and a dab of that" and come up with a perfect cake every time, did not have to concentrate on each action: she was thinking of a hundred unrelated things while she worked.

It is our computers that make many of the seemingly automatic decisions for us that must be made with a fair degree of accuracy. People whose mental computers are not working well are almost without exception ineffective, maladjusted and disorganized. They seem unable to mesh the cogs of their actions to operate smoothly and without effort.

We had an acquaintance who was in a constant state of tension because her computers weren't working properly. She never left the house without wondering anxiously if she had turned off the iron or the oven. She was never quite sure if she had locked the door. Her driving never became automatic: she worked hard, whether it was driving, backing or parking. A couple of hours with her left us fatigued. No wonder she showed strain and tension, just from living with herself!

Such people have never paid enough attention to the routines of living to turn them into automatic skills that will function without constant tending. However, other things can interfere with our mental computers too; one of the most effective "monkey wrenches" is emotionally-caused tension. Emotion causes a slow-down of our computing system—especially negative emotion. It can block us in a myriad of details, affecting our major decisions with earth-shaking results.

Perhaps we have done something that brings us embarrassment. Or we have made a mistake that is hard to remedy. We may be trying to forget a love affair that refuses to be forgotten. A careless or unkind remark has grieved us. Any of these may cause us anxiety, and tension will prevent our functioning well in the daily routines of life. Poor functioning may turn out to be tragic for ourselves and others: traffic accident statistics show an astonishing number of accidents are the result of a driver's emotional turmoil which made him oblivious to traffic regulations. When emotion sits enthroned in the mind, reasoning, courtesy and common sense seem to abdicate. Whatever our roles in life we rely heavily on our automatic computer system.

HELP FOR EMERGENCIES

When I was exploring all possible avenues of reducing my own tensions, I found that the simple exercises of breathing from the diaphragm, writing with my nose and doing the "Rose Meditation" would quiet my mind and release my tensions. Occasionally I found, however, rifts in the human relation field so severe as not to respond to these techniques. A sense of guilt or self-condemnation can occupy our minds so completely that we cannot think clearly or act properly. We get tight and tense all over. Our blood pressure may rise. We may even develop so much toxin that our body metabolism is disturbed and our whole system thrown out of balance.

When this happens, try the following technique. Take pen and paper and write out completely what is on your mind. Do this freely, openly and in detail with no qualms since you are not going to show it to anyone. Psychologists have told us that if we are mad at someone to sit down and write a letter . . . but not to mail it! Tear it up! This technique of writing it out may save your job some time. It might even save your marriage! Counselors call it a "catharsis" and in a sense it *is* a release.

Perhaps this step alone brings only surface release. In that case release the accompanying emotion by taking the emotion out of the experience. To gain insight and understanding of your problem, you must take the emotion out of the experience. Here's how to do it.

Writing it out completely in every detail is the first step. The second is to go back over it and ask yourself, "Now, have I told the truth about this?" This may be a pretty hard question to answer since we all have the tendency to blame someone else for our mistakes. We have adopted the "Willie pushed me!" attitude and it takes a good strong character to face the truth. J. P. Morgan had a favorite remark: "A man usually has two reasons for doing something: the reason he tells someone else, and the actual truth about it."

So go back over what you have written and if you haven't told the whole truth, rewrite it. For the third step, go back over it again and ask yourself, "What was my emotion, or motive in doing this in the first place?" The answer may not come immediately, but if you ponder upon it long enough, the little Voice within will give you the answer. The ancient Greeks believed the solar plexus was the "feeling" center of the body. It does respond to our feelings, and when your answer comes you will get a wonderful sense of release in the pit of your stomach.

Why? Because you are gaining inward wisdom, and inward wisdom builds character, and as you *get* character you *become* one! You become a "character" simply because you have learned how to sit down and ponder upon something until you get the answer, and when you do and have checked all necessary references to make sure your decision is right, you move forth determined to stand on your own conviction. Certainly you will make some mistakes. But how much better to make an occasional error than never to have gotten in motion because you lacked the courage to act on your own convictions! The man who has the courage of his convictions moves out into his world to walk and talk and act with authority so all in his presence feel the truth and the conviction within him.

If the experience you are writing about has had a great deal of bitterness, remorse or regret in it, laugh or cry as you write, as the experience may call for. This acts as a release valve for your pent-up emotion.

MENDING MATERIAL FOR BROKEN HEARTS

Nearly everyone has at some time been involved in a broken romance. The rejected one bears the combined burden of loss, bitterness and perhaps a sense of injustice until such time as adjustment and balance can be achieved. In these cases one should write in detail the whole story of this experience, starting with the first meeting and continuing right on through the entire gamut of experience. When you have completed it, ask yourself, "Now, where did I fail? What should I have done differently?"

The honest answer to this question often takes the feeling of bitterness out of the experience. You can say, "Now I am ready for a bigger and better experience, either with (mention the name) or someone better for me." Do not grieve over the situation, nor blame either, but constantly affirm, "I want either this person back, or someone better for me."

After writing out any situation and getting the answer to it, right then, while I had insight and peace of mind, was for me the perfect time to set my "mental sail" in the direction to prevent a similar recurrence. If it were due to some failure on my part to speak up at the right time I would say words to this effect, "Now that I have insight into this situation and recognize my own failings, I speak my word to know that I shall move out into all situations in the future fully confident I shall be in the right place at the right time, saying and doing the right things at all times. Everywhere I go I shall convey my exact feeling and meaning to the other person and he in turn will completely understand and interpret my meaning."

The use of such statements, which we call our "Science of Happiness thought-directives," will almost automatically improve your experiences in the human relation field. The oftener you direct your thoughts by using them, the shorter and easier your recovery period will be. Write them out and carry them with you for a time. Use a convenient size card; read it over as frequently as possible during the day. I believe you get more good from doing the writing in longhand, although you may be one of those who think best through a typewriter. Words written with pen or pencil demand a cooperation between mental process and muscle effort which seems to impress them more deeply on the subconscious, and they carry a strong personal connotation.

Suppose you have had some personal misunderstanding which you have not been able to clarify. After you have written out your feelings and gone through the three steps as I outlined them, use another Science of Happiness thought-directive: "I know that the Intelligence within me is a part of the Intelligence within (use the person's name) and that he is now becoming aware of my true feelings about this situation. As he ponders upon it, he, too, will gain insight and the rupture in our human relations will be healed. I release this thought, knowing that right action is taking place now. And so it is, for it *is* so!"

You will be surprised how often these situations will be healed and how you will both know that they have been healed the next time you meet the person. Both of you will find your tensions reduced, and the computers of your mind will function normally again.

You will find an added warmth and feeling in all these exercises if, when you write out your mental directives, you will address them to God, or to the Father, or to whomever you turn for spiritual communication. Don't think of the Deity as a Being up in the sky but as a Silent Partner within you, always willing and able to help you. I believe this will give you more conviction. For example, "God, I am ready for a bigger and better experience. I know that your Infinite Intelligence, functioning in me, will guide and direct my ways into full expression. Everything I do today shall be constructive; everywhere I go, I will find understanding and joy; I am grateful that I am a part of the constructive side of your universe."

If you want the computers of your mind to function without the corrosive effect of negative emotions, try all these exercises.

Emotional Maturity Reduces Tensions

Everyone has problems in his life that need to be faced and thought out. Until this is done he is not likely to have self-control or inner security. He has some growing to do before he becomes a mature person who doesn't panic easily when the going is rough.

Joe is an excellent example of an immature person. He is financially poor. He is not satisfied with his job, his status, his home or his wife. He is outspoken in his opinion that the world, particularly his country, owes him a living instead of making things tough for him. He forgets he lives in a country that never lets its citizens starve: a country humanitarian enough to provide medical assistance and hospital care for those who are unable to take care of themselves: a country which through social security provides insurance for the unemployed who have no reserve to see them through an emergency.

Joe is rabid against groups he does not belong to. He is "agin" Democrats and Knights of Columbus (or Republicans and Masons), unions, "niggers" or "furriners"; he resents people with too much education who put on airs . . . airs that come, according to Joe, with a college diploma. It never occurs to him that he is living in a creative universe, and that his present condition is of his own making. Since he believes success is a matter of the right combination of luck and pull, he is not convinced by the examples of many men in our country, who under the most severe handicaps have risen to the pinnacle of success. Joe would do well to study these men's lives and try to figure out what has brought them success. He would discover they all possess the ability and the desire to ponder upon their particular situation until the creative process gave them the answers to self-improvement. Once getting their direction, they were able, through application, to increase their financial stability so they achieved complete independence from the stress and worry caused by lack of money.

ACORNS OF SUCCESS

The great Wanamaker store in Philadelphia had its origin in a pushcart on the lower East Side. The great J. C. Penney chain commenced with a little store in Kemmerer, Wyoming. Al Smith rose from the lower East Side in New York to the governorship of his state. Thousands like Joe who nurse their resentments and harbor their grudges until they are warped and bitter—and consequently filled with unresolved residues of tension—should understand that in our country at least, we need not stay in the environment and on the economic level in which we were born.

A friend of mine who is a successful insurance agent answers the routine question "Well, Pete, how's business?" with a serious "As good as I make it." This man faces facts and reminds himself of them. Many of the leaders in our country today decided upon a goal early in their lives, recognized their own responsibility in attaining it, and applied themselves conscientiously.

One of the best self-starting techniques I know is to inspire yourself by reading life stories of successful persons regularly as they appear in newspapers, books and magazines such as "Success, Unlimited."

What are the factors that keep people from growing and developing as they should? We often hear the excuse that the world is in a hopeless muddle and "what is the use of trying to amount to anything? We'll all be blown up anyway." This creed of futility is inexcusable. The greatest difference between successful men and non-productive ones lies in their desire for self-expression. To quote Lao Russell again, "A man's destiny is determined by his desire for expression."

MAN'S "THRUST" POWER

A man's basic desire, his innate tendencies, his leaning toward an occupation, may take many outlets. Dr. Lee de Forrest, who recently passed on, had a record of over three hundred patented inventions in the radio and television field, and knew early in life what he wanted to do. When his parents urged him to become a minister he said, "No, I am going to be a scientist and an inventor." And he was! He was in the genius category, the fortunate souls whose native ability leads them so strongly in one direction that they have no choice but to multiply their one talent a thousandfold.

Successful men are often so versatile that they could have become equally successful in various fields. One of the functions of our educational system is to explore the individual's potentialities early in his career. The truly happy and stable individuals are those who look forward with enthusiasm and anticipation to their daily activities. These are the men of illumination and vision, who early in their lives determined to "Follow the gleam!" and whose curiosity and perseverance we have to thank for much that is fine in our nation today.

This innate urge for growth and "greater livingness" is in everything. Observe a tree seedling, starting its root in the unlikely soil of a crack in a rock. As it reaches upward to draw certain elements from the air and sunshine, it also sends its roots down to draw from the earth the elements needed for sturdy growth. Before long the persistent pressure of its growth has forced the rock to give way and make room for its expansion. One of the eastern universities tested the power exerted by a plant (as I recall these were lima beans) in emerging from the earth. They found it produced the equivalent of five thousand pounds of pressure which a man would have to exert to get the same results. In this test the plant, instead of taking root on top of an obstruction, as did the tree seedling, started its germination *under* the obstruction, and by its slow and persistent pressure made a concrete slab give way. Atomic researchers are finding that only a tiny amount of power is required to disintegrate some atoms, and that this small amount sometimes succeeds, inexplicably, where a greater amount of power fails.

Man also needs to develop the innate urge within him for expansion, for greater awareness, for better utilization of the abundance of the universe which is all about him. To do this he must apply that type of tension we defined in an early chapter, "the pressure on energy or matter to give it specific direction." This is the right kind of energy-tension, which holds him steady, and gives him stability, and keeps him on the track to accomplishment.

The way he handles this tension is an index of his emotional maturity. His failure to apply this tension intelligently reflects his immaturity.

Three Stumbling Blocks

What other factors keep a man from fulfilling his own God-given right to self-expression? Many counselors believe that such a person has not yet come to any conclusions acceptable to his own mind about the fundamental principles of life. Until he finds answers which are acceptable to him, he will continue to live in a state of confusion, fear or lethargy.

From my own observation ninety per cent of them haven't taken time to ponder upon these problems until they came up with satisfactory and workable conclusions. Let us examine three main stumbling blocks that man encounters in his climb toward maturity and emotional stability.

These stumbling blocks are so intertwined in their ramifications that it is difficult to discuss them separately. However, they are: the fear of death; haziness and confusion about the Deity; a lack of opinion or conviction as to one's relationship to the various intermediaries between God and man.

A young man I shall call Fred phoned asking if he could talk with me. The first interview showed that he was in a state of considerable confusion. Resentment and frustration boiled in him. His work was falling off, he had lost his interests, he was bored with himself. He eventually disclosed he wasn't quite sure that sexual relations, even with his own wife, were "quite nice." In short, he was developing a combination of attitudes which if continued could spell nothing but defeat and despair.

During our interviews it became apparent he had never taken any definite steps toward clarifying his ideas about his own identity as a citizen of the universe. He had only the haziest notions about a Creator—who to him was a combination of a Man in the Sky, a Great White Father, and an Avenging Bookkeeper who kept meticulous files on all his thoughts, words and deeds, to be duly tabulated and totaled at the Day of Judgment. Thoughts about death and the hereafter were swept under the rug as fast as they arose, yet he feared both. Early teachings about Jesus no longer seemed valid to him but he had not found an acceptable substitute.

Was it any wonder that this young man was being tossed like a cork on a high sea, and that he found no stabilizing gyroscope within himself? He was failing as a father also, since his children were now asking questions to which he had no answers. Fred is typical of many thousands today, who are carrying deep within them the burden of emotional tensions caused by such uncertainties.

Man's Early Reach for Understanding

To give us perspective on where we stand today in the long slow spiral of man's ascent from early primitive conditions to the present, let us look at primitive man again.

Through his thinking ability he began to inquire within himself where he came from, where he was going and what had created him. From his observation of his outer world and himself, he came to the conclusion that somewhere hidden behind everything he saw, there had to be a Creator. It was natural that his elementary mind should picture this Creator as a human being like himself, only infinitely larger and more powerful. Since he could not actually see or verbally communicate with Him, his imagination led him to the belief that this Being lived in the sky (which was his concept of infinity) and that He kept a record up there of every man's deeds and thoughts.

As his imagination continued to develop he thought of this Person as an Avenger who, when displeased with his creature's deeds, would visit him with storms, strike him with thunderbolts, rock the ground beneath him with earthquakes and punish him with droughts and plagues. It seemed logical to assume there must be minor gods to take care of different departments of life . . . for rain, fertility, mercy and love and success in war.

Man's need for crops and material things became desperate at times and he developed the notion that the gods withheld these things from him because of their anger and displeasure with him, and that he could appease them through sacrifice. Worship was based on human as well as animal sacrifice. He even promised sacrifice in advance for success in war, thus developing the "bargaining with God" technique still used by some people today. We are all familiar with the famous Biblical story of Jephthah, in the book of Judges, and his rash vow. In return for his victory over the Ammonites he promised the Lord "whatever should come forth from the doors of my house to meet me, . . . for a burnt offering." He was victorious and when his only child, a lovely daughter, came out to meet him, such was his devotion that he kept his vow to the Lord in spite of his natural grief.

Other forms of propitiation ranged from laying the tribe's sins upon a goat, beating it and sending it into the desert to die (we still speak of a "scapegoat") to the sacrifice of doves and small animals for the more minor infringements of the spiritual laws. We see here the earliest attempts of man to assuage his own tensions brought about by his ignorance, fear and sense of guilt.

The concept of many gods prevailed for ages. Around 500 B.C. this gradually gave way to the concept of the one God. He was still an avenging and a jealous God, however, and the Hebrews built up a vast and complex code of behavior for his worship. For instance, there were over 500 regulations to be followed for the proper observance of Holy Days, to satisfy Jehovah, their God.

During this time man's imagination was trying to deal with the weighty question of death and the possibilities of an individual existence following it. Many of our present day rituals and burial customs stem from early concepts regarding the journey of the soul that starts at death. As various religions developed throughout the centuries a great variety of teachings regarding death and immortality were given the people.

Most of the great and lasting religions have taught the necessity of intermediaries between God and man, such as Buddha, Jesus, Mary, Mohammed, etc. While countless millions have accepted these teachings, other inquiring souls have questioned the necessity of going through intermediaries to reach God, and they continued to question it until they came to a definite opinion which they could accept.

BIRTH AND DRAMATIZATION OF GOOD AND EVIL

To encourage men to live harmoniously with their fellows and to improve their behavior in general, leaders in religion based their teachings on the reward-punishment principle. For the just, they painted a picture of an idealistic and eternal life after death. He was assured that infringements on the laws and failure to live up to certain standards would subject him to hell with punishments meted out according to the enormity of his transgressions.

The early church's tremendous power stemmed partially at least from the vivid picturization of the punishment of the damned by such artists as Michelangelo, da Vinci and Raphael who kept the fruits of their misdoings before the eyes of the masses as they attended places of worship. The beautiful presentations of the joys of the blessed furnished the contrast necessary to inspire the multitudes to lives of conformity and docility.

Naturally, with the fear of an avenging and jealous God and the even more constant fear of violating some detail of the prevailing code, man developed a great variety of fears and tensions. We look back on his systems of penances, his use of magic, human sacrifice, masochistic punishment and other propitiations with pity. They seem to us crude and futile. But to him they were logical and efficacious. He was using the only means he knew to achieve a small amount of peace of mind.

OUR EVOLVING UNIVERSE

We have arrived at our present concepts of these things by steps too long and involved to examine here. But we have graduated beyond thinking of the earth we live on as the heart of the entire universe, dominated by a touchy and revengeful God. We see our earth now as only one small planet, among countless billions. When your mind needs stretching, get one of the many excellent books dealing with the immensity of the now-known universe. We must not resist change in our ideas. Expansion does not neutralize their validity: it should only emphasize our concept of the marvelous Mind responsible for the Infinite Creation of which we are all a part.

Our new concepts only confirm our belief that behind this observable universe there *has* to be a Creator. But it does raise the question as to whether beings living on other planets, trillions of miles removed from our earth, worship the same identical God and his emissaries. When we realize that our own small hunk of planet houses over two hundred and fifty different religious sects and beliefs we can only surmise as to the beliefs of inhabitants of other galaxies. In our space age many people have found their mental picture of the somewhat localized "pearly gates in the heavens" changing appreciably. They still believe in them—only now they are further away. The only change is in location, not in principle!

It is not my intention to tell you what you should believe. Our desire for greater illumination is the first step in the development of a workable philosophy. This is, in effect, the same desire that lifted the bean, not *over* the obstacle to its growth, but *through* it up into the life-giving sunshine.

No book can bring you all the answers to the great questions of life, but I would like to call your attention to a few helpful ones. Dr. Smiley Blanton in *Now or Never—the Promise of the*

Middle Years shares with you many wonderful experiences he has had as head of the Psychiatric Clinic of Norman Vincent Peale's church in New York City. Dr. Blanton has been instrumental in helping thousands of persons come to grips with their own anxieties and neuroses. Dr. Frederick Bailes of Los Angeles presents an interesting and helpful approach to understanding yourself and to overcoming psychosomatic problems in his books, *Your Mind Can Heal You* and *Hidden Power for Human Problems*. Among the many writings of Dr. Ernest Holmes of Los Angeles are two small books that are outstanding in their clarity of thought and power: *This Thing Called Life* and *Your Invisible Power*. An excellent book for a time of bereavement is *Ye Shall Be Comforted* by Dr. Robert Bitzer, minister of the Church of Religious Science in Hollywood. This brief list would be incomplete without mentioning the fascinating and scientifically-based book, *The Will to Live* by Dr. Arnold A. Hutschnecker. To me this book is unexcelled for helping the layman to understand the physician's viewpoint on how emotions affect the body. I have mentioned Lao Russell's *God Will Work WITH You But Not FOR You*. This book will lift and expand your horizons; it is filled with inspirational ideas that will add to your joy in living. Interesting accounts of the evolution of man can be found in two books: *The Story of Early Man* by H. E. L. Mellersh (Viking Press, 1960) and *Man's Way: Cave to Skyscraper* by Ralph and Adalin Rinton (Harper & Brothers).

As we look back on primitive man emerging so slowly and painfully from his morass of fear and ignorance, we realize he was constantly forming and re-forming his concepts according to the level of his understanding. We must not forget that our concepts may seem equally pitiful and crude to the man of 5,000 or 10,000 A.D.

We live in an ever-changing universe. If we fail to adjust happily and productively to it our greatest fault will lie not in any erroneous conclusions we may hold, but in our failure to attempt to understand—in our own lack of application to the task of gaining insight that will lift us through the cement and stone of lethargy and ignorance into the Light.

⚡ 10 ⚡

Sexual Maturity —

A Good Tension-Prevention!

We all realize sex is a fertile field for an assorted variety of tensions. Sexual maturity does not just happen as we grow older: it is an individual accomplishment. A person striving for maturity in this area must seek for insight into this complex incubator of mental stress and strain. Only so can he hope to alleviate the self-inflicted traumas most of us experience at some time or other, as the result of fear, ignorance, taboos and superstition still rampant in this field.

THE JOB AHEAD OF US

From time immemorial man's attitudes toward sex have been responsible for much turmoil and inharmony both within himself and in his outer world. Today, sexual incompatibility and misbehavior rank among the foremost causes of tension, family friction, separation and divorce. Juvenile sexual misbehavior, while not new in our social structure, is on the increase, an ever-growing source of trouble and concern to everyone interested in human welfare. Past generations have failed to supply adequate sex knowledge and wholesome attitudes to our young people. Their elders have failed to present them with socially acceptable examples of the true role sex plays in the stable home life. Now we must deal with the mistakes of past generations. Therefore we must present a candid and forthright approach that will educate, inform and inspire multitudes to a different attitude. Through our lethargy and indifference, we have sown the dragon-seeds that are now bearing a crop of hoodlumism, sadism and vandalism. The physical and spiritual health of a nation depends upon that of its individual citizens. We will continue to pay the terrible price of our negligence until we bestir ourselves.

One of the most distressing phases of our sexually-imbalanced national condition is the rise in sex crimes against children. The effect of our overemphasis on sex in movies and other mass media is not limited to children themselves. In every community there are perverted men whose powerful sex urges are inflamed by the obnoxious printed and pictorial material made accessible to them by commercial interests. Their abnormal tensions are increased until they erupt in shocking actions.

Recently on a cross-country trip we met two rare souls: a medical doctor and his wife from Bombay, India. She was a beautiful woman in her native costume, with her long dark braids and expressive brown eyes. They were in New York City for a six-month's refresher course in his specialty, birth control. We mentioned a book on India we had just read which stated that one of the outstanding differences between our countries is that in India men readily and eagerly discuss God. But they become embarrassed and silent when a question involving sex arises. Our Indian friends agreed this is true. Here in America sex is the subject of many conversations, but most people shy away from expressing their own ideas about God.

"A Little Knowledge . . ."

Often, when sex is discussed either conquest, seduction or exploration is involved, and the general tone is smutty, sordid or suggestive. Rarely if ever is there an expression of how beautiful and satisfying a wholesome relationship between man and woman can be.

Usually when sex is the subject, each one considers himself an expert. However, much of his knowledge is a carry-over of "information" he got as a child.

We note the prevalence of this type of misinformation in surveys published by researchers in the field. One that covered a ten-year period in a small college stated men and women students were about equal in their general knowledge of sex but fewer than half were even fairly well informed.

The majority of young people had complete misunderstanding as to the meaning of erotic dreams, thinking they were a part of the male sex cycle vaguely corresponding to the menstrual cycle in women. Three-quarters of the women and men believed sexual desire in a woman ceases completely at the beginning of the menopause. Many believed that they could purchase a cream or some product to increase sexual potency.

These students came from homes that fall into the upper brackets of social, economic and educational background. If they were sent out into the business world with as faulty information they would starve. Neither our homes nor our schools are adequate in providing our young people with the proper education to deal realistically with sex.

If a complete survey could be made of both adults and young people, perhaps not more than 5 per cent of them would know the proper names and functions of the sex organs, or be able to refer to them without embarrassment in ordinary conversation.

This may not seem important to you. Yet the terminology we use for things is an important factor in forming and crystallizing our attitudes toward them. How can we expect to teach respect for the human body, while using the vernacular of the gutter and Skid Row? How can we make our young people aware of the beauty and wholesomeness that exists between the male and female in love, if we degrade it and as parents do not exemplify it? A child learns from his parents on both the verbal and the nonverbal levels of communication. Sex education is one of the thorny problems parents and teachers and educators will face for a long time.

What Would You Do in a Crisis?

Most sexual experiences are accompanied by highly volatile emotions. This fact, coupled with lack of knowledge and fear, causes people to do irrational things, especially when the sexual experience becomes a crisis.

I recall one couple involved in an extramarital relationship. The woman was convinced that she was pregnant. They were desperate, as her husband was due home in two weeks after a lengthy absence. It was suggested she have a frog test to discover if she were actually pregnant. However, after taking a specimen to the doctor for the laboratory test, they panicked and went to an abortionist who agreed to do an abortion for $400.00—that very morning! They paid him and the operation was performed.

The next day the laboratory report came. It was negative. The operation had been unnecessary. Her fear had been so great that it had created the symptoms of pregnancy. The body will try, as faithfully as it can, to reflect the strong mental picture we give it.

This case reminded me of a bit of wisdom: "When knowledge outweighs the fear of a situation, there is a healing." Had this woman been able to calm her fears enough to wait twenty-four hours for the laboratory report, no doubt release from fear would have permitted her body to normalize itself. She would have been spared the lasting effects of psychic shock such an experience always leaves.

Current Antediluvian Concepts

If unhappiness and misery are a criterion, millions of people need to re-examine their sex attitudes. Our concepts of human dignity and progress have been broadening, not in the direction of granting more license to the individual to pursue his selfish goals, but in recognizing every person's inalienable right to a satisfactory outlet for his normal sexual urges under socially accepted conditions. However, an astonishing number of otherwise intelligent people are laboring under delusions and superstitions fabricated centuries ago.

We must eradicate from our thinking such outgrown myths as the madonna-prostitute complex, in which every woman is secretly viewed either as the perfection-on-a-pedestal image or the opposite of this image; the sinfulness of sex knowledge and experience, and the medieval concept that certain parts of the body are evil.

A dear but misguided soul, who belonged to a small fanatical cult once said seriously to me, "Well, we are taught that everything above the waist is sacred, and everything below the waist is sinful." I remarked, "Then how do you account for God, who you say is Love and perfect, falling so low as to create something sinful?" She had no answer.

We must teach our young people that we are spiritual beings living in a spiritual world and that our bodies are vehicles to express our divinity. If this expression is harmonious, constructive and beautiful, then satisfaction and joy will result. We must teach them that conflict between body, mind and spirit brings not only feelings of inharmony and dissatisfaction but attracts experiences that are distasteful and dangerous, and always fraught with tensions.

People have been taught to rely on their conscience, that "little Voice within" to tell them right from wrong. This is good advice *provided* the background of instruction is valid and realistic. We will go to almost any length to justify the beliefs we have held for years.

Other Climes, Other Customs

Our conscience, for the most part, is the product of the social mores and accepted behavior of the society we live in. The mores vary according to the locale and the era in which we live. Socially accepted customs of one part of the world might be punishable by death in another part. What is not "our way" need not necessarily be "the wrong way."

Today, for example, the Bushmen of the African veldt have a very strict set of laws that govern their sexual behavior. It is their custom to betroth a girl baby, perhaps shortly after her birth, to a man who may be from fifteen to twenty or thirty years older than she. This betrothal may culminate in an actual marriage ceremony when the girl is seven or eight years old, but under no circumstance may her husband possess her as a wife until after her first menstrual period. This is a strict taboo and they believe that great harm both mentally and physically would be done the girl if this rule were violated. Prostitution is unknown among these tribes, and promiscuity is rare.

On the other hand a Bushman may divorce his wife by a simple public declaration. There is no stigma attached to this procedure since they believe it contributes to tribal harmony. The African girl and her husband must live with her parents until they have had three children or have attained the age at which they normally would have three children.

Compare this with the present day practice of the Bedouin bride who must display her bed linens on the clothesline on the morning following her wedding night to prove she was a virgin. If there are no bloodstains, the husband has the right to divorce her immediately. This strict code for the woman is the custom even though the husband may have two or three other wives.

In Sweden, however, we find people not only condoning but endorsing premarital relations between their teenagers. This is done with complete knowledge of the parents, in the girl's own home. The Swedes have adopted this social procedure in the belief that it reduces neurosis among the young people, that it gives them a realistic basis for selecting a mate, and that in the long run it contributes to the future stability of the home.

In Tibet and the Arctic regions, one of the finest gestures of hospitality a man can show a traveler who stops with him overnight is to offer him his wife, along with food and drink.

Legal divorce is frowned upon in many civilized parts of the world either by the entire society or by certain religious faiths. It is considered a disgrace to be avoided at any cost. An unwritten code of ethics in some localities permits widespread promiscuity by the men and to some extent by the women, with no social chastisement. To all appearances, those participating in extramarital activities seem not to suffer any detrimental psychological effects.

Triangle Tensions

In America with our Puritan background, adultery is the origin of a great deal of individual tension that often develops into neurosis through an unrelieved sense of guilt and self-condemnation. According to Dr. Kinsey's report, half of all married men are either now, or have been, involved in adultery.

We are not interested here in the moral implications of this subject, as much as in the tremendous tensions built up by persons involved in this behavior pattern. The necessity for deception alone carries with it an overpowering burden of extra tensions. In our social pattern our women are not conditioned to share their husbands with other women. It is doubtful if women ever become well adjusted to any degree of polygamy. Where polygamy is practiced routinely, jealousy among the wives causes a great deal of friction and conflict within the household. The man, whether he is willing to admit it or not, finds himself involved in a constant turmoil despite his scrupulous efforts to be impartial, in sharing his days and nights equally with his wives and children.

Our American woman, accustomed to a higher degree of freedom and independence, is not about to share her man with anyone! She may not at first be consciously aware that her husband has taken up with another woman, but inwardly she feels uneasy and knows there is something wrong. The resulting tension is bound to be reflected in her personality and often in her bodily reactions, impairing her own physical well-being and her sexual response to her husband. Anyone engaged in marital counseling knows that the more relaxed a woman is *before* intercourse, the greater are her possibilities of enjoyment and satisfaction. So if she is in a constant state of tension, realized or unconscious, her cooperation in the sex act will be decreased accordingly.

We should not ignore the tension of the "other woman" in the case. In addition to her ever-present fear of an unwanted pregnancy, she is caught on the horns of a dilemma: she can neither publicly claim her chosen partner for her own, nor can she free herself from the hold he has upon her. Over the weekends when she needs his companionship most, he must be at home with his wife and family. She has not the social standing and acceptance of a wife, neither has she the freedom and independence of the single unattached girl. She occupies a sort of "suspended status" which does not contribute to her emotional stability.

The man enmeshed in an affair harbors tensions also. The possibility of a paternity suit lurks in the background of his mind. He must also constantly guard his conscious thoughts lest he disclose his extracurricular activities to his wife. This strain is disastrous for eventually it affects the free flow of communication between them. When the streams of communication dry up, the drought of discord, tension and multiple misunderstandings follows. Children in the family are quick to sense this inharmony and it spells one thing to them: insecurity! Insecurity and the absence of a normal loving family life are links in a chain of events that make them feel rejected and unwanted. This situation accounts for much juvenile delinquency in upper income bracket homes.

One of the basic differences in the sexes is their approach to the act of sexual union. The wife whose husband is "stepping out" will experience tensions which prevent her from fulfilling satisfactorily her part of the contact.

The husband, on the other hand, seeks intercourse as an instinctive and natural means of relieving the unbearable tensions he has caused within himself. To a man sexual intercourse is relaxing, whereas the woman demands relaxation as a prior condition to its enjoyment. It is evident that when these conditions are reversed, frustration and resentment on both sides are inevitable. Medical doctors are beginning to recognize that the emotions of guilt, self-condemnation and apprehension can cause impotence in the male, temporarily or chronically.

One Solution to Teenage Tensions

A number of communities throughout the nation that have had trouble with the younger generation have been pleasantly surprised at results when these teenagers were inspired to organize, adopt and enforce their own code of ethics. These groups dealt effectively with such thorny subjects as curfew hours, drag racing, use of the family car, dating, graduation celebrations. To the youngsters themselves it has been a revealing experience: they discovered what self-respect means. They kept busy with wholesome and creative activity. They developed pride in being an asset to their community. Such character-building pursuits and self-discipline will stand them in good stead for the crucial dating-mating period.

TENSIONS *Can* FOLLOW THE WEDDING MARCH!

All sexually-connected problems do not automatically cease to exist with marriage. A great many married couples find that even with right attitudes and the desire to cooperate with each other, sexual adjustment still entails many tensions. There are trained advisers and counselors in practically every community, who are available for individual advice; there are many classes in colleges, universities and night schools which are especially designed for this purpose.

Perhaps the day is not far away when everyone who is experiencing difficulties in his sexual adjustments will seek the enlightenment he needs. No part of the shared life of two individuals is more important to them, and indirectly, to their families, than the sex phase. Nothing in creation is quite as wonderful as two persons in love, fulfilling that love by a *total* sharing of their lives. This is the ideal that everyone wants—the "bluebird of happiness" that makes life joyful.

Marriage gives the perfect opportunity for each partner to discover the other's preferences, dislikes, idiosyncracies and responses in the sexual experience. It furnishes the perfect setting to sublimate selfish desires into the welding of a combined satisfaction more rewarding than individualized happiness can ever be. To truly fulfill both partners, marriage must be based on love. Love is the buffer that acts as a shock absorber; it gives both desire and opportunity to help one's mate over the emotional "rough spots" in his personality. It acts as a balance for the inexplicable differences between male and female. Love is the philosopher's stone that works miracles, turning the dross of ignorance, fear and uncertainty into the gold of understanding, harmony and security. The walls of a home built on this firm foundation show few if any of the cracks of tension that tilt so many households today.

POINTS TO PONDER

Here are four points to ponder in times of stress that arise from sexual inharmony.

1. Don't try to solve your problem alone. Difficulties in this category seldom adjust themselves without some effort. Seek good sound, impersonal professional advice. A trained counselor has the advantage of non-involvement in the situation and you will profit from his accumulated wisdom and insight.

2. Try to increase your appreciation and understanding of the wondrous way you are created. Brilliant men of science may devote their entire lives to the study of one small segment or system of the human body and at the end admit the paucity of their knowledge. The "reverence for life" that is Dr. Albert Schweitzer's lodestar and which has guided him to a life of service to humanity, should guide us.

3. Recognize the fact that a Creator who created the world male and female would not punish his own creatures for using any part of that creation constructively and in the way it was designed to be used. Accept the teaching that we are punished *by* our mistakes, not *for* them! This is a big step in the direction of emotional and sexual maturity. Remember that the judgment which we mete out on our own and other's doings is affected by the degree of our own maturity.

We must realize that the use of the sex organs in the way they were designed to be used, between male and female and in the spirit of love, is in no way contradictory to the Laws of Nature. Primitive man, half-savage that he was, recognized early in his development that incest was a greater crime even than murder: murder killed one individual while incest eventually would kill off the whole tribe through deterioration of the life factor. He placed a taboo on homosexuality because he realized it was contrary to the Laws of Nature. Punishment for breaking sex taboos was severe, for the wise old men of the tribe knew that perversion of any kind was a threat to the continued existence of the whole tribe.

4. Learn, once and for all, the great lesson that when man dashes himself against the Law, it is not the Law that is broken, but man. It is man's violation of the Law, usually through ignorance, that engenders conflict, confusion and unbearable tensions in him. The man who knows the Law and refuses to conform with it builds and must carry with him his own particular brand of tensions until such time as he decides to take active steps to free himself of the burden.

The American Institute of Family Relations, 5287 Sunset Boulevard, Los Angeles 27, California, has many helpful pamphlets on sexual education. Among them are two twenty-five-cent pamphlets: "Preparing for Marriage" and "Building Sex into Your Life."

Also, parents with small children will appreciate a simple but effective course of six lessons: #201; Home Study in Social Hygiene—Guidance in Sex Education," by Roy E. Dickerson, price $2.00. "Sex, Love and Marriage" by Dr. Paul Popenoe, 50c, is an informative approach to adult problems. Both are available at the above address.

Here are two more excellent books: "Love and the Facts of Life (What Every Teenager Wants to Know)" by Evelyn Miller Duval, published by Association Press, N.Y. "Everything You Always Wanted to Know About Sex (But Were Afraid to Ask)" a Bantam Book written by Dr. David Reuben.

How to Live with Yourself —
And Like It!

Are you on good terms with yourself? Do you like yourself, as a person?

If we do not like ourselves, if we cannot accept ourselves, if we feel inwardly unworthy of the good things in life, we are defeated before we start. All of our social and business contacts will be tinged with the embarrassment and awkwardness that a lack of self-acceptance brings. We will be in a constant state of tension.

Whenever I saw evidences of this lack of self-acceptance in my counseling work, I tried to get to the bottom of it. Only by dealing with the cause can we help dissolve any type of tension.

THAT PRIVATE CREDIT RATING

What is the best way to test your self-acceptance? How do you accept—or reject—a compliment? Many people cannot accept favorable comments about themselves, simply and graciously and without self-consciousness. Too often they actually reject kind words by claiming they are not true! This places the well-meaning giver of the compliment in a most unfavorable light.

I met a charming little girl of six the other day; she had such a sweet and wholesome way about her I was sure she must be pretty, and I told her so. Instead of acting coy or shy, she said sincerely, "Thank you!" Test yourself, the next time someone makes a complimentary remark to you. If your first impulse is to contradict the words, check yourself before you speak! Accept it graciously. You will feel better about it, and so will the other person!

What's in a Name?

Another simple test in self-acceptance is the attitude towards one's name. Test others first. Suppose you are in a gathering with several people you have not met as yet. Go over and introduce yourself. Observe how seldom the majority reciprocate. You may have to ask them point blank. You may be surprised again how many will say, "Oh, hello—I'm Marge" or "Max." So you pick up the ball again and ask "Max who?" But it's no use. If he is like many I have met, he will respond uneasily, "Oh, just Max . . . that's what everybody calls me."

Or he may come up with an odd-sounding name mumbled so you can't understand it anyway. All this byplay means this person holds a mental image of himself that does not measure up to what he secretly would like to be. He has a sense of unworthiness, inadequacy, guilt or an implied apology for living. These people are uneasy and diffident, timid and self-effacing; seldom do they make a worthwhile contribution to any gathering.

Now why do we feel this way about our names? After all, they are an important part of our total personality, being the label by which we are identified. So a dislike or inner repudiation of our name is bound to cast a shadow on our self-acceptance. There are many reasons why people dislike their names. Take Max, for example: he may have been reared in a family of foreign extraction. Perhaps his parents did not feel the urge to learn the language and customs of their adopted country, and if they were in the minority in their neighborhood, the children were the butt of censure and ridicule while growing up.

Although they may leave home and establish themselves as solid citizens, there is always a nagging remnant of childhood embarrassment connected with their name. If they had examined the foliage of the family tree as they got older, they might have found a limb or a twig there they would have been proud of! There are ancestors to be proud of in all races and this is particularly true in this country where the virtues of all nationalities have combined to make America what she is.

Many people in this situation have legally changed their names, and with the new name they have taken on a new personality more to their liking. When budding movie stars are given a new name by their managers, they too, often adopt a whole new set of personality traits to fit the new "image." Many people adopt a nickname and use it regularly, preferring it to their own. Women have an advantage in changing their name by marriage. All this is a part of the self-acceptance pattern and reverts back to the "imagery" and role-playing we have discussed.

Here is another test of self-acceptance. When someone has tried to pay you for service, have you refused the payment? Have you said, "Oh, that's all right," or "Never mind, let it go"? Later, did you feel sorry for yourself because they had failed to insist on compensating you? This episode reveals your feeling of unworthiness. When you can't bring yourself to accept something that is rightfully yours, it is a good indication that you are not accepting yourself. It is as necessary to be a good receiver as a good giver.

A Surface Job—Guaranteed to Peel!

Some years ago a book that discussed our "mental equivalent" became quite popular. If we lack the *inner* acceptance and response to a set of ideas, it is most difficult for us to really assimilate their outward appearances and make them a part of us. Take a person who suddenly comes into a sizable amount of money. If he has been in limited circumstances all his life, he seldom can adjust to new riches well; in a matter of months he may find himself back where he started, financially, with the possible addition of new and artificial tastes no longer possible to indulge. His inner consciousness of abundance did not coincide with his windfall, and he had neither the judgment, knowledge nor proper advice to enable him to accept it.

Our inward acceptance of ourselves, like a magnet, brings forth its equivalent in our outer environment. Unconsciously it resists change. I knew a man who owned a nice hotel in an outlying district of Los Angeles. As it prospered he got the urge to do something for people living in squalor and dirt on Skid Row. Accordingly he bought two hotels in that depressed area and an apartment house in a slightly better neighborhood. As one set of rooms in the apartment house was vacated he tore out the frayed rugs and shabby furniture, replaced them with new furnishings, and painted the rooms. He offered it to tenants at no increase in rent. This gave him a great thrill, since he felt it was a fine humanitarian gesture.

But his illusions were soon shattered and his eyes were opened to the futility of trying to adjust people's attitudes toward themselves from the outside. Tenants moving to the refurbished quarters were dissatisfied. In a few days they asked for their old ones back; they "didn't feel at home"! In despair he gave up his project and contented himself with providing the kind of surroundings they could accept. Most people cannot be helped until they are ready. To fully accept any change, it must feel normal and this normalcy is the result of gradual growth. No veneer applied to the outside will stick!

WE TELL THE WORLD!

Do you think other people are unaware of your acceptance of yourself? It is more evident than you think. One symptom of a person's low esteem of himself is careless personal grooming. The person so lacking in self-respect that he goes around unbathed, unattractively dressed and with slovenly posture is announcing his sense of his own unworthiness to the world. Casual attire does not justify dirty finger nails and spotted ties. Habits of good grooming should be made a part of our young people's heritage. It is just as important to the ego to be scrubbed and presentable when alone, as when in public.

The English government officials, during the years of active colonization of the far reaches of the British Empire, adhered to their custom of dressing for dinner every evening. Their tables were set with silver and china and candlelight, even if they were the only white men on the outpost. This not only kept up their own morale, but established their caliber as representatives of their government in the eyes of their native constituents. Their own self-respect and self-acceptance was fostered by this deliberately-followed custom.

"A man is known by the company he keeps," and "Birds of a feather flock together" are two old sayings that tell us the company we choose to associate with is an indication of our own self-acceptance. Show me the company you seek when in a strange town for a time, or the guests you invite into your home, and I will give you a fairly accurate idea of the status of your own self-acceptance.

THE ROOTS OF THE MATTER

Enough about symptoms. Let's talk about causes of these effects.

Why are so many people ill at ease when they are complimented? Why are so many people ungracious receivers of expressed commendation, or compensation for services performed?

One reason may be that in the past many religions have taught the virtue of extreme humility and humbleness. They have adopted the "man is a worm in the dust" attitude so wholeheartedly that their followers cannot see themselves in any other light. We are evidently beginning to swing away from this trend, and to move in the direction of recognizing man's potentials and capacities, as well as his achievements. But much damage has already been done in thousands of lives through the families' custom of downgrading the individual's accomplishment. Their intentions were sincere and good, since they felt their attitude was necessary for a true and acceptable worship of God. But we see the remnants of it yet, in the self-derogatory, apologetic and self-effacing bearing of many people.

Another mark of the person who cannot accept himself is a timidity that hinders his free self-expression, and a fear of what other people will think or say about him. This person is not only the "dot in his circle," he is also the perimeter. The spotlight of his attention is always on himself. He shuns spontaneous actions or words, fearing he may be criticized. Even a small "boo-boo" while out among others causes him untold embarrassment and mental anguish, and consequently, tension. In his effort to be inconspicuous he speaks almost inaudibly, or mumbles his words and talks through clenched teeth. Apparently it has never occurred to him that the mistakes he worries about having made are universal in the process of growing up. You will find this person holds unrealistic standards of perfection for himself.

One more reason for people's not accepting themselves: their hidden sense of guilt. Sometimes this lies so deep as to be hidden from themselves as well as others. If they are aware of it, it may be based on some detail in the past that is minor in proportion to their present suffering. Sometime during their childhood, for example, they may have developed an unusually sensitive conscience, or they may have been reared in a home with unrealistic sets of values, which has resulted in a constant self-chastisement.

Upon bringing these ogres into the light of reason and examining them, they may find their worries based on minor infractions that they should have long ago dismissed as lessons and experiences and forgotten. But these people are so lost in the jungle of emotion that it takes a tremendous effort to cut through it, in order for enlightenment and insight to pierce it. Not long ago a young man of thirty, with a wife and family, told me he was a grown man before he realized that all people are faced with the same questions regarding sex as had bothered him as a young boy. This revelation did much to straighten out his thinking.

WHERE TO?—WHEN YOU "WANT OUT"?

A favorite escape hatch for people submerged in the depths of self-rejection is daydreaming. If they are in circumstances that seem unchangeable, dreaming of the future appears to be their only escape. Like a tranquilizer, this works for a time. But if people continue to live in daydreams long enough, they become lost in a fog of confusion. Since the teens are the time of life we do most of our daydreaming, let's see how a teenage boy is apt to use his "escape hatch."

Most of us look back on a fairly tumultuous adolescence. If our teenager is an average boy, he sweats through periods of embarrassment and humiliation because of his own physical awkwardness. He has not yet achieved social aplomb, and is always "putting his foot in his mouth." He feels no one really understands him and he lacks the words to put his feelings into expression so they can. He suffers a great sense of rejection because any small infringement on his ego is interpreted as a body blow. Like a threatened turtle, he learns to withdraw into his shell at the slightest provocation, there to brood upon his pain.

So we find our teenager building a series of "castles in Spain" at this point. The usual daydream will take him away from home and apron strings to some vague, faraway destination from which he will return, grown-up, handsome, self-assured and famous. He pictures himself received with admiration and respect by all the "twerps" he left behind, who now are proud to say they "knew him when."

This dreaming is quite natural. Many of us continue some of it, even into adulthood. Where is the dividing line between a healthy imaging which will inspire to future accomplishment, and a fruitless, frustrating waste of time?

That point seems to lie at the place where the gap between our daydream self and our everyday self becomes so marked that we cannot identify with both simultaneously. If our teenager is taking definite steps to bring his self-image into focus and hence into reality, these steps form the link between the two selves that keeps him in balance. His dreams prod him into constructive activity in the direction of his goal, particularly if he has the encouragement of understanding parents and teachers. If he has dreamed of returning from his travels as a famous singer, for example, and if he is utilizing his time and effort by taking vocal lessons, he will have a great sense of satisfaction in this outlet. As he advances in his study he will find doors of opportunity opening to him. The firm ground of self-confidence and actual performance will be under his feet.

The only way our blueprints of fantasy can be turned into the "more stately mansions" of achievement and security is through our own application and perseverance.

Some Practical Suggestions

In your own efforts to build up your self-confidence, don't minimize the power of giving yourself suggestions. We are all "suggestible" and can follow our own suggestions as well as those of others. Also, don't fear that you may set yourself unattainable goals: we are also self-limiting mechanisms. We set our own boundaries on what we can achieve, and they are realistic ones for the most part, based on our potentials. Rely on the old adage, "What man can conceive, man can do."

What is your present self-acceptance "rating"? A good way to test it is to stand in front of a mirror when you are alone and use this technique of self-suggestion: Say, "I", repeating your own name, "as a person have the qualities I can accept and admire, and which the world also accepts and admires. Daily I am becoming a more successful, effective and likable human being." I am offering this only as a suggestion, to get you in the mood to experiment . . . use your own words that feel good to you. This is an excellent way to discover your weak spots, if you do not already know them. If you can't say something complimentary to your reflection without mentally ducking, you know this is a weak place that needs attention. Shaping words to fit your own psychic soft spots will help you overcome that weakness.

Suppose you feel unloved, lacking in beauty, grace, intelligence. Use another Science of Happiness thought-directive: "I, Mary Smith, accept myself because I am a nice person. I like my name. I am grateful for my many friends. I am a lovable and radiant individual, fully confident of my own divinity. I know that as I constantly, honestly and truthfully apply myself and seek right action in every situation, the truth I find will set me free of the bondage of the past and any limitation I may have had."

Is this technique applicable in the business world? You bet it is! The young salesman, self-conscious about making calls or soliciting business by telephone, or whatever his problem may be, can use it very effectively. And if he *will* use it for thirty days, consistently, he will discover a new power and a new confidence surging up within him to bring him the results he wants. He can use this Science of Happiness thought-directive to start with, adjusting it as he goes along to suit his personality and needs: "I, Sam Jones, am a creative, thinking and effective individual. I know that salesmanship moves the goods our economy produces and gives employment and financial stability to thousands of families. My profession of salesman is a necessary and a respected one in our free enterprise system. I now turn my attention to my day's activities. I apply myself, knowing my creative process will bring me the answers I need to present myself and my product most effectively.

"As I move out into my business world today, that world responds to me with the same degree of confidence I have in myself. Everywhere I go, I am accepted in every way. I align myself with the constructive side of Life, physically, mentally and spiritually, and so aligned, I am becoming the successful person I wish to be."

12

"Sleep, That Knits the Ravell'd Sleeve of Care..."

(SHAKESPEARE)

Insomnia has plagued people throughout the ages. King Saul called for the shepherd boy David to lull him to sleep by playing on his harp. We must realize that during a lifetime our sleeping habits will vary. We may go through a period when we are unable to sleep with the same depth or awaken with our customary vigor and vitality. We need to remind ourselves these phases come and go and do not continue indefinitely. The amount we worry about our insomnia is one of the factors that determines how long it will last. When these sleepless moments come, face them realistically. Do whatever possible to dissipate the strain and stress causing them.

Since we are a triune being of body, mind and spirit, insomnia is a three-headed problem. If it persists too long we should explore its roots accordingly—physically, mentally and philosophically.

If lack of sleep is robbing you of vitality you might start your search for the culprit at the physical level.

WHY DON'T WE SLEEP?

Physical exertion helps reduce mental tension. Our forefathers who worked hard in the field and forests all day, our grandmothers with a garden to hoe, a house to clean, butter to churn, wool to spin and cradles to rock, were so physically exhausted that at bedtime they were ready for sleep.

Today modern society does not give us even a fragment of the physical activity necessary to dissipate our natural physical energy and give us the wholesome "tiredness" conducive to sound sleep. As a result countless numbers of people are resorting to pills that will dull their minds chemically and slug their bodies into insensibility.

Many have learned, to their sorrow, that sleeping pills are a dangerous crutch that if used long enough will lose effectiveness. They must then increase, perhaps double the dosage to get the same results, and this is a dead end road. There is a limit to what the human system will tolerate.

How much better if you consider sleeplessness a by-product of some type of tension and concentrate on reducing that tension, intelligently! Common sense tells us a sound body, given proper food, rest and daily exercise, is bound to function better than one permitted to degenerate into a soggy mass of protoplasm infiltrated with foreign chemicals, inadequately purified of its accumulated toxins. A well-cared-for normally functioning body is going to require less sound sleep than the body that is sluggish and only half alive. However, if there is a physical cause for lack of sleep, a medical doctor should be consulted.

Do not misunderstand me. In saying a healthy body may need less sleep, I am not suggesting you hypnotize yourself with the idea that four or five hours of sleep will do. Even if this is supposed to be the hallmark of genius, face the fact that you probably tick better on seven or eight hours, like the majority of the human race. Then see what you can do about getting it. Don't listen to the "pep artists" who try to convince you that by chopping three or four hours off your sleeping time and tacking them onto your working day, you will become a huge success. People who have tried this have generally found themselves paying a tremendous price for such foolishness.

ATTACK INSOMNIA ON THE PHYSICAL FRONT

Make regular exercise a "must." You may find it difficult to schedule workouts at a gymnasium, time-wise and financially. But the average person will not find it necessary to do this if he will take a few minutes a day to "be good to himself." Can you walk briskly up a hill? The heart experts tell us the little extra exercise to the heart muscle is beneficial, using discretion, of course. Take it easy at first and increase your gait comfortably as you go along. This mild hill climbing is recommended by such experts as Dr. P. D. White, ex-President Eisenhower's physician, and Bernarr MacFadden. Deep breathing, swinging the arms and perhaps singing while walking will further drain off surplus nervous energy and make you ready for sleep.

Physical exercises in your own living room could be the answer, not only to sleeping better, but to enjoying more pep and vitality. Recently we advertised a davenport for sale. Next morning our door bell rang, and a pleasant gray-haired man came bounding up our stairs two at a time, announcing as he reached the landing that he would like to look at the davenport. During our conversation we remarked at his pep and vitality.

He said, "You know, I am seventy-two years old! Ten years ago I retired from business. I needed to, I was really tired! The doctor told my wife confidentially that my health was failing. I suspect they both thought I wouldn't live too long. I felt miserable, physically and mentally. When I woke up mornings I hated to face another day without the routine of action.

"Then one morning I tuned in to a television program on physical fitness. I said to myself 'What have I got to lose? I'll see if this man's ideas are any good.' Well, I tried them out and they seemed reasonable to me. I stayed by it, doing my exercises every morning. Do you know, within a month I felt like a new person? Today I have more pep than when I was forty-five. I sleep like a baby. I have a good appetite and eat anything. I am back in the business world, owning and managing my own apartment house."

As he was leaving he turned back for a parting shot: "Life is great, when you have the good health to enjoy it!"

This man had a priceless possession . . . joy in living! And joy is contagious. Life can be great for *you* too, provided you have a healthy vehicle. If necessary develop your own setting-up exercises. The simple exercise outline in the chapter on "How to Stop Smoking" helped me reduce leg twitching and a feeling of fullness in the stomach after going to bed.

Before retiring loosen up the neck, shoulder and head muscles with the technique given in the chapter, "Getting the Kinks Out of Your Neck" by "writing" with your nose such words as Rest, Sleep, Relax, Yawn, etc. Use any words that seem right to you. Then go to bed and as you put your head on the pillow, give yourself the suggestion that you are going to enjoy a good night's sleep. If you should awaken during the night don't lie there worried and tense. Get up at once, sit up awhile and repeat the exercises that helped you drop off to sleep earlier.

Here is a real "quickie" to flatten the abdomen and to induce all-over relaxation in only ten seconds: stand with your heels and head touching a door casing. Take a deep breath, and exhale. Now pull in the diaphragm and try to make as much of your body touch the door as possible. See if you can make the calves of your legs, your waist, back and shoulders touch the door, take a deep breath and hold it while you count ten. Then release all your muscles. You will be surprised how good it makes you feel and how relaxed you are afterwards. Now go back to bed. You should be able to get several more hours' sleep.

THE MENTAL ASSAULT

When it comes to relieving insomnia, everybody is an expert. You will be advised to take everything from aspirin, a hot drink, a cold drink, a snack, a hot bath, a cold shower, a night cap or a good detective story. At times of extreme stress if you need a pill or a drink, take it! But as a rule, *my* advice is to stay away from the artificial and unnatural crutches and learn to rely on your own resources. Trial and error will teach you how to concoct your own treatment.

The greater the anxiety, the more elusive sleep. If we use our minds actively and creatively just before going to bed, we may find it difficult to turn off the creative process. We may have encouraged a bad set of sleeping habits by permitting ourselves to fret about unsolved problems and vexing situations as soon as the light is off. An exciting play on television may prove overstimulating. Children are especially susceptible to programs of violence, horror and crime overtones, and will often respond with nightmares. Better control and direction of the last hours before bedtime, for both children and adults in the family, could well result in better sleep for all.

There are many devices for "turning off the mind." Here is a helpful one. After you are in bed and quiet, lie flat on your back without a pillow, eyes closed. Now mentally, with your nose draw a line from the heel to the little toe on your right foot. Follow it on, tracing the outline of each toe separately, in detail, picturing the nail of each toe as you do it. When you reach the big toe follow the line down the instep to the heel. Now move over to the left foot and do the same thing. Make your motions slow, deliberate and exact.

Imagination is a wonderful aid to sleeping. Nearly everyone has a favorite scene that has pleasant memories connected with it. Picture such a scene in your mind, or make up one you have never seen: a gray ship floating at anchor on a gray sea, a cold mountain stream dashing over the rocks, a desert, with its violet and gray and mauve shadows, lying motionless under a late summer sky. The "Rose Meditation" in the chapter on "Freeing Your Mind From Tensions" is unsurpassed for help of this kind.

So—You're Awake!

Should these devices begin their effect slowly, don't be discouraged. Say to yourself, "Well, if I don't sleep tonight, I will tomorrow night!" The body has its own way of getting an adequate amount of rest and sleep. If you get a textbook on one of the subjects that bored you the most in school—geometry, history, English—and read it with concentration, your mind will rebel, become tired, and you may find yourself asleep before you know it. You might even pick up some information in a few nights of this kind of reading that will be more beneficial than the extra hours of sleep you are trying so hard to snare. Or, you just might be one of those "geniuses" mentioned earlier, who really need only four or five hours of sleep!

SOME SPIRITUAL TRANQUILIZERS

For centuries people have found comfort and a sense of relief in praying aloud. Keep a book of selected readings and prayers at your bedside and make it a habit to read them before going to sleep, preferably aloud. The spoken word has a way of sinking deeper into the subconscious than the silent one, but use whichever is the more comfortable for you. You might add to your collection, "Prayer at Evening" from Dr. Robert Bitzer's excellent little book *All Power to You.*

A PRAYER AT EVENING

"I thank Thee for the day just finished. For Thy Guidance which directed me—for Thy love which surrounded me—for Thy courage which led me on. I thank Thee for the good which I have experienced today. For the loving kindness which I met—for the helpfulness upon the way. I thank Thee for the opportunities for service which this day brought. For the cooperation and friendliness—for everything that made life bright.

"All that I have done this day I leave in Infinite Mind. I rejoice that Thou wilt take all of my honest efforts and increase their effectiveness. I know that all that I did in my sincerity Thou hast accepted—that each effort will be augmented—that any activities which should be redirected or straightened will find their perfect fulfillment.

"I know that Thy Guiding Wisdom will direct every effort toward the attainment of my perfect life in Thee. That I can never deviate from my God expression. That I can never deny my Divine Re-

ality. Nor can anything ever obstruct the flow of Perfect Life
through me.

"I rejoice that my increased understanding makes me wiser, more
tolerant and firmer in my conviction that God-in-me finds perfect outlet.

"I give thanks for the Perfect Rest of this night and that refreshed
and renewed I shall meet tomorrow with New Inspiration, New
Life and New Power."

You will find this next "spiritual tranquilizer" an almost sure-
fire antidote for your insomnia. Here is the essence of an article
I (Eve) wrote that was published in the "Science of Mind" maga-
zine, August, 1955.

Count *THEIR* Blessings!

"A popular song some time back had as its theme the counting of your blessings, instead of sheep, to put you to sleep.

"Instead of counting *your* blessings, try counting those of your
friends and relatives or neighbors. Take anyone in your circle of
association . . . regardless of their circumstances. Go over, in
your mind, one by one, all the things he has to be grateful for:
look at each of these things in turn . . . his health, his vitality,
his interest in others, his lovely home, his charming wife . . .
and be grateful that these are his. In all this itemizing be sure you
see him utilizing each of his blessings for greater good to himself
and others.

"Be sure to keep your mind open and receptive to all 'good
thoughts' about each person, and don't let any thought of con-
demnation or criticism creep in. When you have used up all the
possibilities you can think of for one person, turn your thoughts
to another. Perhaps this one is undergoing a "down draft" in
health or finances or love: picture him as he was when everything was right with him, happy and active, prosperous and se-
cure. See him this way in the future.

"You may not have time for more than two or three of these
"blessing inventories" before you lose yourself in sound sleep.
Your attention has been directed away from yourself and your
affairs and the body becomes completely and totally relaxed, as
does the mind when freed from stressful thoughts. We are told

our bodies do most of their rebuilding while we are asleep. . . . No wonder! It is not hampered then by the action of the conscious mind with its apprehensions, tensions and strains. It is under the control of the subconscious mind entirely, with its marvelous and unfathomable ability to operate it.

"There are some other by-products of this little exercise, aside from the fact it will help you to sleep better. You will regard each person whose 'inventory' you have taken with different eyes, the next time you see him. You will be aware of a deeper and more personal interest in him. You will unconsciously be on the look-out for more of his "blessings" to count when his turn comes up again! You will even feel somehow connected with his progress and well-being, almost as if you had a hand in it! Don't mention your little sessions to him, by the way! However, he will feel your increased friendliness and warmth and will respond to it, but he need not know the reason for it.

"This is especially true if you will count the blessings of some-one with whom you are not on good terms. They tell us that one sure way to overcome a hate, a grudge or a resentment, is to do a service for the person concerned. You can neither harbor nor send negative thoughts toward one whose blessings you have counted in the stillness of the night hours.

"You start the morning with a clean slate—a good beginning for a new day!"

Misunderstanding —

Master Builder of Tensions

A disreputable-looking man and a little boy with long shaggy hair entered a barber shop. A customer was there, already in the one chair. When it was vacant the man put the boy in it and he said, "I'll just go down to the drugstore on the corner for a minute while I'm waiting for you," and out he went. When the boy's haircut was finished the man still had not returned. The barber said to him, "Where do you suppose your father is?" "My father!" exclaimed the boy. "That's not my father!" "Well, who is he then?" inquired the barber. "Oh, he's just a man I met down the street that asked me if I wanted a free haircut."

We should be aware of our "assumptions." They can cost us money. Sometimes, from the vagueness and meagerness of our communication efforts, one would think we expect others to read our minds.

A woman was given a traffic ticket for making a left turn without signaling. A car behind had collided with hers. When she was hauled into court she was so indignant that the judge finally said, "After all, madam, the man who ran into you had no way of knowing you were going to make a left turn." "Well, he should!" she retorted. "I've been making that left turn every morning for thirteen years!"

Our assumptions that we have made ourselves understood are sometimes just as ridiculous as this lady's.

Do You Jump to Conclusions?

Faulty communication can be more serious in its results, too. Walter Hill, the manager of a department in a large store who had been with the company for many years, was involved in some trouble with a new superintendent. Rumors were flying that there would be changes made. Tension was high; the department manager felt very insecure. One day the grapevine had it that an executive with lots of seniority was going to "get the axe." An hour later the secretary of the new superintendent called Walter, saying, "Mr. Hill, the superintendent, Mr. Brown, wants to talk with you in the morning." Then in a semi-confidential tone she added, "Something about abolishing a department, I think."

Walter froze. He knew without asking it was his department that would be "crossed off." His hands and feet grew cold. He felt weak and ill. He could not eat lunch and finally went home in the middle of the afternoon. He was too ill to keep his appointment with Mr. Brown. Two days passed, then a week, and he was still at home.

The general manager of the store, a good friend of Walter's who had known him a long time, called on Walter one evening. "Congratulations, Walter!" He shook Walter's hand vigorously. "Mr. Brown has decided to consolidate three departments under one head. It means some of the younger men will be laid off, but you are to be the new head of the big department! The decision was made because of the fine years of service you have given the company."

Walter's recovery was phenomenal. He looked like a new person as he reported for work the next day. Had he had a bad heart his assumption could have been tragic; as it was, he learned a valuable lesson. He had acted before he had all the facts pertaining to his action, and his fear had made him run before he could obtain them. There is no question that his assumption had caused his tension!

MEET "MR. G.S."!

Our tendency to assume something is true without having sufficient evidence to back it up is one of the pitfalls we are warned about in the study of General Semantics. This fascinating subject was first presented to the world in 1933 by its founder, Alfred Korzybski with the publication of his *Science and Sanity* which is still today the principal textbook. Korzybski's premise is that we fall down in our human relations woefully because of the unscientific structure of our language, and the way we use it. While most sciences have mediums of communication that are precise, accurate and dependable, this is not true of the language in our daily living.

Someone has called words "the devices we use to veil our meanings." By including a chapter on General Semantics, which I will hereafter refer to as GS, I hope to make more people aware of our own responsibility in the realm of communication. To have harmony in our human relations there must be an even flow of give and take.

If we will look at communication as a "two-way street" in which it is as necessary to be understood as to understand, it may help us become aware of how we fail in both.

WHY BE UNDERSTOOD?

It is estimated that we communicate from seventy to ninety per cent of our waking time. We are deluged in an ocean of words. The average person today probably uses and listens to more words in a day than anyone at any time in the history of the world, simply because our modern mediums of communication— printed word, radio, television, telephone—have made it easy to communicate. The tempo of our times puts efficiency at a premium. How can we estimate the time lost because of faulty communication? How much money is lost? How many lives, and how much unnecessary tension is caused? Let's say the percentage of accuracy in giving, receiving and carrying out instructions is 70%: someone has to pay for the other 30% which, with possibly more care, greater attentiveness or more specificity could have been chalked up on the asset side of the ledger.

Business and industry has awakened to the vital importance of accurate communication. Most business consultants agree good communications is a vital factor in establishing better business-management and management-labor relations. Recently more attention has been paid to breaking down the barriers existing between specialized branches of our economy: each has a vocabulary unintelligible to other branches, and they must be translated into mutually understandable terms in order to work effectively together.

SOME BARRIERS TO UNDERSTANDING

The meaning of a word is something that happens within an individual. It does not dwell in the word itself, like a larva within a cocoon. Semantics deals with the meanings of words themselves, but General Semantics (GS) helps us deal with the meanings which exist on the nonverbal level—the meanings we "read into" words and sometimes into situations.

A minor difficulty springs from the fact that many words in our language have multiple meanings. The foreigner, attempting to learn English, is invariably confused to find himself using the right word, perhaps, but in the wrong context. For the most part we unconsciously extract the right meaning from multi-valued words but when we make a mistake the results can be disastrous.

Take the word "run" for instance; we are told it has more than one hundred meanings! The word "fast" will vary too, as you apply it to a horse, a color, a woman, the rope that ties a boat to its mooring, or the abstention from food. Firms have run into difficulties with interpretations of the word "credit" in their own departments: someone asks for credit, a man comes in to establish credit for a loan, the editor of the house organ wants his authors' credits listed, a payment has to be credited to an account.

"Velocity" means simply "speed" to the layman. But in the frame of reference of the space scientist, it may mean something quite different.

This variation is even more noticeable in our slang expressions. The word "hot" can mean a dozen different things, depending on the circumstances in which it is used, the occupation and status of the speaker, the experience of the listener. A "hot" diamond, for instance, is quite a different thing from a "hot" tip at the race track.

Thus all knowledge of our outside world reaches us through the filter of our own nervous system, colored by our past experiences, our needs and desires and our immediate surroundings. It is small wonder we often get a partial or a confused picture of reality. Much of the time we use our senses according to our motivation.

We look at our wrist-watch to determine the time. Our attention is on the position of the hands. But at the time of purchase we were concerned with the shape, the size and cost. After wearing it awhile, it is likely we never thought of those things again. We want utility. An envious person, however, or a would-be robber, cares little about its function—he is interested in the number of diamonds, their size and brilliance. The watch is exactly the same; the variety of reactions to it is based on interest, background of experience, need and motivation.

So it is with all our experiences: the "perception center" turns them into usable information for us!

Is Seeing Believing?

Some wise person said, "We see what we are." This can be applied to the other senses as well. If a turned-on electric fan were shown to a primitive savage and he were asked to describe it, he might conceivably say it was a whirling circle or a disc—in his own words, of course. To him it would look like a solid flat piece of metal. If a cameraman photographed it, his picture would bear out the native's description, since it also would show a disc.

Now switch off the electricity. What has happened to the disc? It appears as four obliquely placed metal blades, not even remotely resembling a flat circle of metal. This is enough to put the whole matter in the realm of "magic" for our primitive friend. But because of our familiarity with fans and some knowledge of the laws of physics, we adjust nicely to the changed appearance of the object.

I remember my astonishment as a child when first I observed railroad tracks converging in the distance to a point. This was one of my first object lessons in the truth that "you can't believe everything you see." Lesson #2 came when the stick I thrust down into a stream seemed to have a crook in it, where it entered the water: when I pulled it out, the crook was not there!

Through similar episodes we learn about our world; as adults we should apply them to modify our own opinions and judgments. We should teach our children to recognize that many things are not what they seem, and never to make snap judgments. The greatest Teacher of all warned us to "Judge not by appearances."

A woman, peering through her bedroom curtains in the early hours of the morning, saw the high school girl who lived next door coming up the walk to her home, staggering and half-carried by a middle-aged man. The neighbor could hardly wait until morning to spread the word around that "Betty came home drunk from a party, with a strange man, old enough to be her father!" Betty and her family were gone, and the gossip spread for several days before the word came back that Betty had suffered a sudden attack of a rare and little-known illness which affected her muscular coordination: that her parents had taken her to a distant clinic for medical care and that the "strange man" who had helped her up the walk was the father of the girl at whose home the party was held. Almost irreparable damage was done to an innocent girl through a gossipy and ignorant woman who "guessed she knew a drunk when she saw one!"

Don't "Paint Yourself into a Corner"!

How sure are we of our opinions before we voice them? How wise are our judgments? Someone has said "A wise judge never renders a verdict until all the evidence is in." How do we get "all the evidence" about anything?

Unless we are aware we are "identifying" in this way, how can we hope to correct it? When we "identify," semantically speaking, we talk and act *as if* what we say about something is the truth. We call a person who habitually "identifies" a dogmatist: he is always positive in his statements; he will brook no contradiction; he is *sure!* He has never learned to leave himself a "loophole" through which he can gracefully back out of his flat statements. He is the one who says, "Cats hate water!" The next day he may read of someone's tabby taking a swim, with a picture in the morning paper to prove it. His statement assumed he knew about all cats in relation to their aversion to water. He was guilty of using an "allness" statement. One should never make an "allness" statement for the simple reason that "the map is not the territory, the label is not the thing" and no matter what we *say* about anything, it can never be the whole truth about it. Failure to recognize this procedure can lead us into trouble and tension. There are no exact duplications in nature: leaves from the same tree, even identical twins, have their differences. No two snowflakes have the same pattern. So when we treat a single unit of a large classification according to our emotional feelings, we are in difficulty. Through our indiscriminate labeling (Japs, niggers, Jews) of individuals, we disregard differentiating characteristics that if recognized, make for peace and good will among men— and many fewer tensions!

The teenager, trying to wrest permission from his reluctant parents, says "Aw, Mom, all the kids are doing it . . ." or "Everybody is going . . ." Pin him down to a specific account of just what "all the kids" means, and he can't name more than two or three. This is one of the best techniques to make people see the ridiculousness of their statement and to break them of using such "allness" phrases.

In time, too, we will come to recognize "loaded words," as dangerous as the "unloaded gun," that can trigger off temper, tension and irritation . . . such words as "never," "ever," "always," "every time," etc.

There is another tension-trap for the unwary—that of using

the "Law of the Excluded Middle." To people who habitually do this, A is always equal to A, and nothing else: never to B, nor to A_1 or A_2. Things are either black or white . . . no wishy-washy in-between grays for them! It's wrong or it's right . . . no middle ground! The emotion-racked lover on the witness stand tells the judge, "I told her . . . she'd have me or she'd have no one!" Our mental hospitals and psychiatrists' offices are crowded with people who thought they had to have "success or failure" (again, no in-betweens for them!), poverty or wealth, loneliness or togetherness, and a hundred other "either-or" situations which meant they had created for themselves dilemmas which could have no possible or realistic solutions.

WHAT MAKES US ACT AS WE DO?

Our lives are filled with events from which we learn, and the majority of them are accompanied by various emotions. If there is no emotional involvement or content to an experience, we tend to forget it. The episodes fraught with deep emotion we remember best of all. It is this "conditioning" process that is responsible for most of the instantaneous responses we make to life's stimuli. We tend to respond to an outside happening with the same set of emotions we had on first encountering that type of situation.

A child of three, eating dinner with his family, is caught up in the vortex of an angry quarrel between his parents. He doesn't know what it is all about, but the loud voices, the harsh words and glowering expression on their normally loving faces shocks him. His digestive process stops. His heart beats harder, and he suddenly leaves the table and relieves himself of the tomatoes he has just eaten. There may be few if any repetitions of the scene, and it gradually fades from his memory. But it is engraved deep in his "un"- or subconscious. As an adult he claims he is allergic to tomatoes. He says they are too acid "or something" and evidence seems to bear this out, for every time he tests his "tomato-tolerance" he becomes ill. Years pass, and his subconscious functions faithfully as a time clock whenever the "tomato" lever is pressed. By now he feels no sense of loss as he "passes up" the tomatoes.

What can we learn from the tomato story that will help us with our tensions? When you are irritable from contact with another person who seems to rub you the wrong way check yourself carefully to find the cause. Sometimes just a physical similarity to an unloved relative can "tee you off." Perhaps you are even allergic to the name of the person, for the same reason. These reactions are as hard to control as a sneeze. They may be based on conditioned reflexes such as I have mentioned, or they may spring from misunderstanding. Again, check to make sure you understood the other person. Did you by any chance assume he meant something, and then go off in a corner, figuratively speaking, to nurture your hurt feelings, your anger or resentment?

"By Your Words . . ."

Our language and the way we use it reveals our true selves. Through GS we may learn many devices to help us define our meanings and to gain insight into the real meanings of those about us, although they are concealed on the nonverbal level. We have touched only a few of them here and you may wish to explore them further as a means of controlling and regulating the traffic on your own two-way street of communication.

We live in a changing universe and we can be sure of only one thing: nothing remains at the same point for long! "You cannot step in the same river twice," runs the old proverb. We all vary from day to day, almost from hour to hour, depending on our chemical makeup at the moment, our morning mail, the temperature and humidity, our dinner menu the night before—a hundred factors combine to make us what we are at any given moment. Yet we will insist on treating Mr. $Smith_1$, by which we mean the Mr. Smith we saw today after a year's absence, the same as we treated Mr. $Smith_2$, which is Mr. Smith as we knew him. What happened to him in that year may not show on the outside, but has changed him drastically on the inside. The smart secretary remembers that $Boss_{10.00\ A.M.}$ is quite a different guy from $Boss_{4.45\ P.M.}$. As a parent, before you dish out rewards and punishments to $Bobby_8$, remember he is not the same boy as $Bobby_6$ was. $Grandma_{80}$ may be more forgetful and more irritable than Grandma$_{65}$ was, so increase your leniency toward her.

This device is called "dating" and is a very useful one. Learn to use, at least mentally, quotation marks to indicate many things . . . that the words have a questionable value or an unusual use in the context in which you are using them, or that they are words that have no definable reality in themselves, such as "mind," "space," "time" and "eternity." Learn to hyphenate words to show you see their inter-relatedness. Learn, above all, to use the magic words "it seems to me" to bridge the gap between you and the other fellow's sensitive feelings. This is a great tension easer.

14

Three Magic Rules That Can Free You from Worry

I never knew a person who did not worry, sometime, to some extent, over something. It seems we are not constituted to operate totally without some worry; we feel concern, we know anxiety, we "turn things over in our minds." Without some worry at least, we would not function as effectively as we do. And having said so much *for* worry, these are all the favorable comments I have about it.

Someone has said "Worry is like rocking in a rocking chair: it gives you something to do but it gets you nowhere." Worry, uncontrolled, unrecognized and non-productive, is at the root of much of our tension . . .

If you are a victim of the habit, ask yourself, "What am I worrying about?" When your answer is clear in your mind follow it with another question: "Have I sought good advice about this problem?" After pursuing our own line of thinking with no results, we are wise to seek help. Whether we need technical information, such as is found in the library or in experts' writings, or personal help, the advice of a disinterested person is often priceless: his view of the situation is impersonal and therefore unbiased. Sometimes all we need is additional information or knowledge to dissipate the fog of uncertainty and indecision. In the courts of our land, ignorance of the law is not accepted as an excuse. It is the same with our self-made trials: we suffer the consequences of insufficient knowledge in inward turmoil, confusion and frustration.

Then if you are still under pressure and cannot see your way out, try these three rules to help you banish this type of worry from your life forever.

THE #1 RULE

The first one is our familiar Golden Rule. Its name is appropriate because gold for centuries has been the symbol of something rare and valuable. This rule is the essence of all the great religions, past and present. Buddha said "Minister to friends and familiars in five ways: by generosity, courtesy and benevolence, by treating them as one treats himself, and by being as good as his word."

Confucius taught: "What you do not like when done to yourself, do not do to others." Hinduism: "Let no man do to another what would be repugnant to himself." Judaism: "Take heed to thyself in all thy works. And be discreet in all thy behavior. And what thou thyself hatest, do to no man." The Sikhs were instructed: "As thou deemest thyself, so deem others. Then shalt thou become a partner in heaven." And the followers of Taoism tried to follow the injunction: "Rejoice at the success of others. And sympathize with their reverses even as though you were in their place."

The Christian religion's teaching is: "All things whatsoever ye would that man should do to you, do ye even so unto them: for this is the law and the prophets." A universal application of the Golden Rule would solve all our human relation problems.

Add to these words the commandment of the greatest human relation expert of them all, Jesus of Nazareth, "Love thy neigh-

bor as thyself" and you have two of the strongest possible founda-
tions for a worry-free life. Our modern science of psychosomatics
is beginning to catch up with this teaching. Recognizing the
efficacy of this advice, it has proven the emotions of resentment, hate, anger, are tension-producing and responsible for
many of our physical ills.

If the basis for your worry shows some element of friction
with another person, you must examine your own part of the
transaction in the light of these rules of conduct. As long as you
concern yourself only with self-justification and defense, you will
not dissolve your worries.

But say, "Now, where in this situation did *I* fall down? Where
did *I* fail to do the loving thing?" With your answers will come
that release of inner tensions that will enable you to enjoy again
sound sleep and worry-free days.

THE #2 RULE

After you have applied the Golden Rule as a measuring stick,
use the Silver Rule.

This is not as well known as the Golden Rule, but it is important, too. It tells us to "Do unto yourself as much as you do
unto others." Frequently in my lectures I use one of my favorite
sayings, "You can't be good to anyone else until you are first
good to yourself." There are some people who have such an
over-emphasized compulsion to be of service that they make it a
virtue to ignore their own good. They are constantly busy with
their "unselfish" efforts to do for others.

While it is good to help others we must remember also—our
primary responsibility is to keep ourselves functioning on the
highest possible level, in body, mind and spirit. Of course we are
not truly compartmentalized, as we have seen, and this is why,
when we allow ourselves to become deficient in one of these
phases, the others also suffer. And so do those around us. We
must be careful not to indulge in the martyr-complex.

The mother, overly conscientious about having a clean, orderly
and well-run home, can without realizing it perhaps, drain herself of her physical energy so that she has little vivacity, cheerful-

ness or optimism with which to greet the members of her family on their return home. The father who feels that he must spend sixteen hours a day making a living for his family should re-examine himself and his activities. Surely, having time to be with his children, to help his wife in the household routines, also to recoup his vitality for the next day, is just as important as having two Cadillacs in the garage, a swimming pool in the back yard and a $50,000 mortgage on his possessions.

In all things, "balance" is the key to success. It keeps you from swinging too far one way or the other. Every man and woman has this decision to make . . . to put *first* things first, and to do them in the order of their real, not their seeming, importance. The person who is being good to himself in the true sense can always be of more service than the one who is dragging at the heels from a mistaken sense of duty and responsibility.

The woman who attends her community and charitable activities after her own house is in order is a more relaxed and efficient helper than the one who leaves undone her own chores so necessary to a smooth-functioning household. Knowing your own affairs are taken care of before going out into the world to help gives a tremendous release of energy.

All this is important. With more women coming into the business world we are facing a crisis in which half of our citizens are attempting to hold down two jobs . . . that of wage earner and homemaker. Unless our women are alert to their responsibility to be good to themselves first, both of their jobs will suffer. So will the human relations angle of both jobs. Many are preoccupied in turning in a good job at the office, then coming home to meet the demands of routine household chores. Their energy and desire to give loving care, time and attention to their children is at a low ebb. We cannot afford to deprive our nation's children of these necessities.

One of the most obvious sources of tension is the feeling of "over-load"—of being required to do more than we are able to do. A pile-up of this kind of tension, with no relief, spells trouble. It must be broken with planned periods of recharging your physical and spiritual batteries.

THE #3 RULE . . . THE HARD ONE!

The Iron Rule is aptly named: it is hard to follow, for it says: "Do not do for anyone that which they can and should do for themselves."

Personally I feel this rule is a little severe, for most of us love a certain amount of doing for others, and I would like to modify it with the words, ". . . unless doing it brings real happiness and good to both parties." We all know it is possible to rob people of their independence and initiative, their chances of learning from their own experience, and their maturing process in general. The baby who is constantly picked up each time he falls while learning to walk will lie there and scream until he *is* always picked up.

"We learn by doing the thing," Plato tells us. Many a mother who has consistently made herself and her resources too available to her family, has discovered one day, to her dismay, that they do not have the ability to stand on their own feet. She had ignored the Iron Rule! We must use wisdom and discernment in giving love and service. Overindulgence and protectiveness are not signs of love but of our own lack of self-discipline. The financially successful father who showers his son with "all the things I couldn't have as a kid" is doing the boy a great disservice. They both may pay a high price in later years for his lack of insight.

Hugh is a young man who is now reaping the effects of the withholding of the Iron Rule. The idol of his widowed mother, he lived a sheltered adolescence with no duties or responsibility and without brothers or sisters to balance his maturing process. His expenses to a private school were paid from the savings account that was part of his father's estate. His mother's circle of contemporary friends did their part in "helping" Hugh, lending him their cars, finding good-looking girl friends for him and inviting him often to dinners and parties.

He graduated from school, looking at the world not only as his oyster, but secretly thinking someone should open its shell for him. At his mother's death he was shocked to find the family finances depleted, the necessity of finding a job immediately, and a world that had no interest in "doing things" for Hugh. When I saw him he was bitter and disillusioned. Already for his "relaxation" he was turning to the solace of alcohol.

Thousands of Hughs could have been saved for a life of usefulness and independence, had the Iron Rule been applied early in life.

"No Takers" for Worries

"Misery loves company." Or at least it loves sympathy. One of the shocking lessons we all learn is that the world is not interested in hearing about our worries. "Smile and the world smiles with you: weep and you weep alone" is as true today as ever before. Don't make the mistake of assuming that because someone says, "How are you today?" this permits you to tell them . . . particularly if you are ailing. Happiness is contagious, but so is unhappiness. The world prefers not to be subjected to the virus of your worry or anxiety. It has enough of its own.

Offered for Adoption—Three Good Helpers!

We all carry the responsibility not only of making a living but of being happy, so that we will not contaminate those about us. We also have another responsibility—remember?—that of not allowing others' unhappiness to contaminate and infect *us!* Of course we should lend an ear, when someone's tensions demand the outlet of expression. But we must keep ourselves from becoming emotionally involved with him. This would be of no help to them; quite the reverse. By keeping your own mental and emotional equilibrium you can ask him questions to bring enlightenment on his situation. Thus, in helping him to help himself, you will have applied all three of the Magic Rules.

An eighty-year-old friend of ours was losing his hearing. His family purchased a hearing aid for him at considerable expense. But he had trouble adjusting to it and the sounds he had not heard for so long seemed loud and distressing to him. So he put it in his dresser drawer and left it there. However, he still mourned because he missed so much conversation.

One day while visiting the family I shouted to him, "Grandpa, where is your hearing aid?" Sheepishly he admitted, "In my dresser drawer!" I said, "What do you suppose it is hearing in there?" He chuckled at the thought of the hearing aid, lying there in his drawer, trying to hear something.

We are as inconsistent as he, when having the means and tools to add to our understanding and enjoyment of life, we keep them shut up in a dark corner of our minds, instead of taking them out and adapting our lives to them.

Nothing will work until you work it! Not even these Magic Rules.

I didn't *say* it would be easy!

And Now, to Work!

If you are a worrier and want to change, you should have several ways of dealing with your worry habit. If one doesn't work, try another.

An extremely successful business man of my acquaintance uses a "Worry Box." This is a small box with a slot on his desk at the office. Whenever he finds himself worrying about something, and not getting any place with it, he sits down where he can be quiet and writes out his problem on a slip of paper. This he drops into the box.

Every Wednesday morning he comes to work thirty minutes early, and opens his Worry Box. Problems that have been solved during the week and no longer need attention he drops into his wastepaper basket. Those still pending he puts back into the box. During the rest of the week he thinks as objectively and constructively as he can about them. If more information would be helpful he reads up on the subjects, seeks good advice and studies new angles. Then mentally he sets them aside and refuses to worry about them again until the following Wednesday.

He says it always surprises him to find ninety per cent of the slips are thrown away . . . these problems have either been solved or they have ceased to be of any concern. *The "imp" in importance for each of us is the significance we attach to the things we worry about*. Of course this changes from day to day.

Look back a year and you will find it hard to enumerate all the things you worried about.

Suppose you use a Worry Box. Suppose you decided to do the worrying about the slips on Wednesday mornings. What would you choose to think about, between Wednesday mornings? Since we can think about anything we choose, this is a logical question. Paul gave us some good advice when he said, "Whatsoever things are good, lovely, true, beautiful and of good report —think on *these* things!" If your mind is filled with *"these* things" it cannot also be filled with worry, for you can think of only one thing at a time.

WE BECOME THAT WITH WHICH WE IDENTIFY

Think kind, loving and serene thoughts and you will have loving, kind and peaceful experiences. You will draw them into your circle of awareness as a magnet draws steel filings. Face a barking dog and it will run from you. Face your worries openly and courageously and this action in itself will help you solve them.

One of the best ways to make your worries "run from you" is to sit alone in your own home or office, and frankly confide your problems to God. For best results, you should do this aloud. It must be done as thoroughly and effectively as you are capable of doing it. Include every detail connected with your problem, even if it seems irrelevant at the time.

Gradually you will find certain angles of your situation grouping themselves together in your mind, along with possible solutions. This clarifying process will reduce the tensions that bind you to your problem.

Your worry may be of such magnitude that you feel incapable of handling it . . . It may be concerned with radioactive fallout, the hydrogen bomb, the need for world disarmament, etc. In that case, read again the wonderfully effective little prayer of Alcoholics Anonymous.

"Give me the serenity to accept the things I cannot change: the courage to change the things I can, and the wisdom to know the difference." If you will adopt this with sincerity and honesty, you will find it one of the best ways to overcome chronic worry.

HAVE DONE WITH WORRY!

We are constantly carrying on inner conversations with ourselves. We may debate a course of action with ourselves, offer a rebuttal and render a decision for the ruling side. We weigh the sides of a question, almost as if we were two persons in one. Talk to yourself about your worry habits!

If you have been in the habit of inviting negative thoughts—jealousy, envy, resentment, self-pity, injustice and malice—think of these as intruders in your mind. The old Chinese saying fits here: "You cannot stop the birds of the air from flying over your head, but you need not let them nest in your hair."

Face and define your troubles. Gather knowledge about them from every good source. Confide your worries to God. Do all you can about the situation that is causing them. Don't contaminate your friends and loved ones with them. Even if you don't have a real "Worry Box," every evening before you leave your office or before you go out for the evening, stand before an imaginary Worry Box and drop your worries into the slot in the top, one by one. Evict these unwelcome thoughts. *You* are the master of your mind. They cannot stay if you bid them leave.

Then, in place of the sedatives or tranquilizers you may have been taking, try another of our Science of Happiness thought-directives for a month. Repeat this directive over and over whenever you find yourself worried. You will find it a potent and rewarding "worry-chaser."

A SCIENCE OF HAPPINESS THOUGHT-DIRECTIVE

"I am ready now to look at my so-called mistakes as experiences through which I grow by gaining insight and understanding. I look at other people's mistakes this way, too. I forgive everyone in my human relations in the past and in the present. Worry, care and anxiety have no place in my life.

"I relax, from the tips of my toes to the top of my head. As the stars above me wheel in their orbits in precision and perfect order, so my thoughts are in perfect order. I am in harmony with my Universe. Every cell in my body responds and attunes itself with this harmony.

"I am at peace."

15

How I Became Acquainted with Tension

How Would YOU Deal With It?

To make the rest of this book more meaningful to you, try for a moment to grasp what it would mean to you, were you to have the experience I described in the first paragraph of this book. First, to face, daily, the certainty that the visible world as you have known it will shortly no longer exist for you. Secondly, to have this become a stark reality within three months.

As you enter vividly into this experience by proxy, you will be better able to understand the role our senses play in the formation and alleviation of the super-tensions that play havoc with our lives.

We have examined together the sources of information coming to us from outside ourselves which we must perceive if we are to function well as human beings. I doubt if many of us realize how dependent we are on our senses until we are deprived of one of them. The person who has had a cataract operation or suffered an attack of glaucoma from which he recovered, is probably far more appreciative of his vision than the person who has never been deprived of it.

A QUESTION OF COMPENSATION

Right here I would like to clear up a common misbelief in this regard, at least according to my own point of view. The assumption is often expressed that if one sense is lost, the others will compensate for it. I agree that this is true to some extent, but I would like to make clear one stipulation: it is true *providing* man applies himself to bring it about; it does not happen automatically, any more than the act of giving physical birth automatically makes a woman a mother, in the true sense of the word.

For example: suppose a man has been employed picking up hundred-pound sacks of cement all day, and he loses one arm in an accident. Back on the job again, he can learn to pick up sacks again, with only one arm . . . but only if he applies himself to the project. The remaining arm will not automatically demonstrate the strength to do what was formerly the work of two arms. The same principle applies to the loss of a sense. We know, for instance, that anyone expecting the sense of feeling, or touch, to compensate for the loss of his sight would be sorely disappointed, because the sense of touch could not possibly give more than a fraction of the information afforded by the sense of sight.

But the "feeling" effectiveness can be increased by application so it grows in efficiency. This, added to the increased awareness of the other senses, enables the person to function more normally than without this application. If it seems I am laboring this point unduly, it is because I feel it is so tremendously important.

THE STARTING LINE—WHERE YOU ARE!

The urge of such an individual to achieve normalcy under his particular circumstances can be attributed to only one thing: the deep desire to survive . . . to live . . . and to grow. True, these desires often become submerged in the depths of fear, frustration, confusion, despondency, anxiety, etc. But however deep these troughs, when sooner or later the desire to live surges up again, the person picks up the pieces and starts his climb upward.

At any rate this is what happened to me. In spite of the fact that I was only thirty-six years old and knew I would never see, that my conscious mind told me I was finished and I could not see how I was ever to earn a living, deep within me was that desire to live. Faintly at first, but with ever-increasing intensity came the desire to be active, to be of some value to the world— even to enjoy life again, in spite of what the world called a handicap.

In order to do this I realized I would have to get over the fear of not being able to see. This in itself was a big step. For as I worked on it I was surprised to find myself gaining additional information from my other four senses.

At this point I began to be actively interested in the whole problem of tension. I found by experience that I had to be relaxed in both mind and body before my other senses would relay information that would be of help to me. In other words, I realized that when my body was relaxed I was more receptive to the stimuli coming in on the receptors of my other senses and I soon knew that only the harmony of my *whole* being would permit me to do a good job.

Just recently I found a definition of the brain's function in the Encyclopedia Brittanica that intrigued me, because it fits so perfectly into the concept about myself which dawned on me at that time. Here it is: "The brain's job is to weld the body's component parts into one consolidated mechanism, facing as a united entity the changeful world about it." I think this is a wonderful definition. It says in such compact and meaningful words what I was trying to achieve, minus one of my "component parts."

Visualize—Then Practice!

I set about my project of functioning normally in a systematic way. I began by visualizing just how I wanted to look as I was walking down the street using my cane. How did I wish to appear? A bent-over, fearful, cantankerous individual? Or did I want to walk with my head up, a cheerful expression on my face, feeling confident of my own ability to take care of myself? The decision, of course, was obvious.

So I took the next step.

After getting myself in the right frame of mind through visualization, I would go out to the sidewalk, carrying my cane. I walked jauntily, swinging my cane nonchalantly, but making sure it hit the grass at the side of the walk on the down stroke to tell me exactly where I was. I practiced this hour after hour and soon found I could walk in the manner I wished to present myself. Other information began to come to me of which I had been previously unaware.

The first bits came to me through the sense of feeling. Not so much tactile feeling, as the sensing of temperature and humidity changes. I found myself able to tell when I came to the end of a building by the difference in the air pressure and air currents; (in the afternoons, the buildings retained the sun's heat, and the air between them and in the alleys was cooler). Any change in the atmospheric conditions registered on the nerve endings of my face, and helped me "navigate." I observed this long before I read on my Talking Book Machine about the "facial vision" which the blind often develop.

I was able to feel the trees as I walked past them, but noticed it was much harder, and sometimes impossible, to detect an iron post, or a traffic signal post. I had the feeling that organic things, living things, give off something which makes them more noticeable to our nervous system than metals, and wondered why.

MY LESSONS CONTINUE

I learned other things, too. Stepping out of the house in the morning I could feel the warmth of the sun on my face and this told me it was a fine day; the absence of it told me the day was cloudy. I was inspired by the sense of smell many times: the fragrance of a rose bed, the tempting aroma of freshly-baked goods as I passed a bakery, the pungent smell of bay rum and witch hazel from a barbershop.

As I walked I would hear the whirr of the cobbler's sewing and buffing machines, a mechanic fixing a car in his garage. I remember how excited I was to find that the combination of smelling, feeling and hearing had cooperated to tell me the car I was passing had just been parked: I felt the heat from the engine on my face, I smelled the hot metal and radiator, and heard the faint crackling sound as the metal cooled. I had many such experiences and the thrill of self-discovery was a soul-satisfying one.

My courage increased as time went on and I decided to venture beyond my own block. If a person relying on a cane to "see through" approaches a curb with the cane straight up and down in front of him, the cane can tell him the height of the curb through the sense of touch and hearing. But you don't come up to a curb that way. You approach it with your cane at an angle in front of you, and only the tip of it touches the very bottom of the curb. I found that when I was completely relaxed and co-ordinated my foot would always rise to the top of the curb, regardless of whether it was two, four, six or ten inches high. I never stubbed my toe.

It was almost as if my feet could see! I have often thought about it: do the atoms in my feet actually have a kind of sight? Do they have an intelligence of their own? I began to speculate about this to friends and acquaintances, and sometimes the expression on their faces was so plain I was aware of it, even though I didn't really see. So I decided to stop talking about it.

Nevertheless I was aware that there was Something over and above the sense of touch and hearing that was giving me guidance. As I continued to venture further afield, I found that *if I were relaxed* this Guidance was always present. All I had to do was listen to it. Many times, going down the street alone in Los Angeles, San Francisco or Podunk, the Knower within me, as I called it, would say, "You had better check this . . ." I would stick out my cane, and sure enough, there would be something I should know about. Many times I was virtually led from one side of the sidewalk to the other by this inward knowingness, and would later find that whatever I had thus avoided would have been a hazard to me.

We Must Acknowledge the Source

As time went along I developed a little technique that has given me a world of satisfaction: it was just saying, "Thank you, Father!" every time I was aware of the working of this Guidance. It was an expression of appreciation, and the recognition of this inner Intelligence in me. It seemed even to increase my ability in this direction. I soon found I was using it automatically whenever information came to me through any source. This is still one of my richest experiences.

Often we are blocked from conveying our true feelings, from expressing our true thoughts, because our choice of words or terminology differs from that of the other person. This is especially true in the field of spiritual experience and religion. To some, the term God, Infinite Mind or Infinite Intelligence may be foreign and unacceptable. To others the expressions The Knower, the Little Voice within, Intuition or E S P may rankle. To me, these are all the same. I use them here interchangeably, hoping that somewhere along the line one or more of them will ring the right bell with you so you can say with feeling and sincerity, "Yes, I see, too . . . I understand what is said here."

✎ 16 ✎

Clairaudience, Clairvoyance,

Telepathy, Intuition

After coming to Los Angeles, following the loss of my sight, I attended many classes and lectures on subjects new and intriguing to me. Many of them opened up vistas, particularly of the mind. While the following episode is not my own personal experience, it is such an unusual example of clairaudience I want to share it with you.

Let us define our terms. Clairvoyance means the ability to sense things taking place at a distance, either in the sense of time or space, as if "seeing" them happen. Clairaudience is another kind of inner knowing that can best be described as "hearing," though not with the physical ear. Persons who experience this are at a loss to explain how they know things; it is as if they heard a voice telling them, yet not an actual voice.

Several years ago when I used to do counseling, my phone rang one morning. A feminine voice said, "Do you know anything about mental telepathy?" I said, "It all depends on what you want to know about it." She related one of the most fascinating stories I have ever heard.

She was born on a ranch in a western state, located in a rural section with no modern conveniences, such as electricity. While she was in the eighth grade at the rural school she suddenly began to hear a song . . . so clearly she could distinguish both the words and the tune. She began to sing it to herself. Her mother remarked they must have a new teacher for someone was teaching the girl to sing "a real pretty song." The daughter replied, "No, it just came to me. I even wrote it down."

As time went on, other songs came to her and as she sang them, her mother asked, "Did these come to you, too?" The girl said, "Yes, I hear the words and music all the time." The mother began to get a queer look on her face and when the neighbors dropped in to visit she told them about the songs, intimating her daughter might be "teched in the head."

The next year the family moved to town so the girl could go to high school. They purchased a radio and in great excitement gathered around to hear it play the first time. A man's voice came over the air, and his first song was the one she had first heard and sung while at the ranch! Words and tune were identical. The family recognized it at once.

They were filled with fear, wonder and amazement, and as they listened to succeeding programs they heard other songs she had been singing. The program was that of a well-known crooner in Hollywood and she decided to write and tell him of her experience. She received no answer to that letter nor to any she wrote subsequently. She determined that as soon as she finished high school she would go to Hollywood and see the famous singer personally.

When she called me she had been in California for two years. Lacking experience or training, she was working as a housemaid, and she was very emotional about the whole thing. I finally asked her, "What is the emotion back of all this? What is upsetting you?" She immediately denied having any emotion.

Then I said, "Is it possible you are burned up about not cashing in on your ability?" It was as if the question had pricked the balloon of her emotion. Finally I asked her who she thought was the most likely to have created these songs . . . a group of trained and competent persons directing their attention and talent toward song-writing as a business, or she, a young and totally untrained girl out on a western ranch? And if *they* had created them, and she had simply tuned in on them and picked them up as a radio receiving set picks up a broadcast, was she entitled to recognition as their author? She began to understand that the famous singer had no obligation to her regarding the songs. Her common sense told her that she had not acted logically but had been driven by greed and jealousy.

She finally said, "I guess that's right; I see now what is bothering me. I felt a great injustice as if this man had taken *my* songs and then had refused to see me." Then she asked, "How much do I owe you?" I told her, "Just let your conscience be your guide." "All right, I'll send you a check," she replied. She never did, and I don't care. Because I learned something that day I would not take anything for . . . I discovered another verification that there is "one great field of Intelligence, available to all men," as Emerson said, and that we can all draw upon it. But we must draw it through *us,* because, as I explained to the young woman, this is really the source of our creative ability. It is activated and set in motion by our willingness to sit down and ponder upon something until it begins to give us the answers, whether to a business problem, concocting a new recipe or inspiration for a new song. Once conceived, they are available to all who "tune in."

For years this girl had suffered the pangs of a demoralizing, devastating sense of injustice—self-inflicted, it is true, but nevertheless one that tore her apart day by day. She had been in the grip of a real "super-tension"! Her focus of attention had been on the wrongs she thought had been done her, instead of being directed to efforts to develop herself into a fine person. She should have been using the technique of, "Thank you, Father, for the unusual ability I have had." *While you are busy being grateful, you can't be bitter!*

Is This Telepathy?

Attending classes and lectures, I made many wonderful friends. Among them was a group of six or eight who often went to church together on Sunday mornings, then had lunch and exchanged ideas on the sermon. I often went to church on the bus with a friend who lived near me. When I was ready I would call her, saying I was leaving for the bus stop and she could join me there.

This particular Sunday when I called she was just about to notify me she could not attend that morning. She had had a long distance call from her daughter who was attending a girls' school in the East. The daughter had a chance to ride to California with friends for Easter vacation and she called to get her parents' consent. The mother had refused to give it until she discussed it with her husband who was somewhere in the East on a business trip. She was now waiting to hear from him.

She had called his eastern office to locate him but as it was Sunday, had had to call the chief clerk at his home; he had informed her that her husband had been in New Orleans the Friday evening before. He was expected in Cincinnati on Monday morning but no one knew where he was spending the weekend. I said, "Well, since you can't call him, why do you wait for him to call you? Why don't you come on to church?"

"Oh, no," she said. "You won't believe this but my husband and I have worked out a little system. When either of us wishes to get in touch with the other, all we have to do is think of the other real hard. Before long, the other person picks it up and calls. I know it sounds silly but it works. I don't know how to describe it other than a subconscious communication between us that somehow becomes conscious. I am sure he will call me before long."

I rang her up about 4:00 o'clock and she said, "Well, he called me!" Her husband had been tired after the New Orleans meeting and needed a rest before attending another meeting in Cincinnati Monday morning. So he and a friend decided to spend the weekend in a cabin in the Kentucky mountains. Shortly after noon Sunday he said to his partner, "Dick, this may seem silly to you but I have a strong feeling my wife wants to get in touch with me. This has happened before and when I get the feeling this strong I should do something about it. I will have to go down to the valley to a phone." When his wife answered the telephone he said, "Honey, have you been wanting to get in touch with me?"

Now, my friend had received the call from her daughter shortly after 9:00 A.M. which would make it noon in the east. She immediately tried to contact her husband at his eastern office, had to call his chief clerk at his home, and when she found she could not locate her husband, she set about sending her message to him in their own way . . . on the subconscious, nonverbal level. He picked it up in Kentucky shortly after noon, his time.

To me this is another example that neither time nor distance affects this miraculous power we have.

How Do We "See" These Things?

You may have read the book *The Mystery of the Hidden Crosses* by Upton Sinclair. It is the true story of a woman living in Los Angeles who had visions throughout the years of the location of buried crosses. These crosses were the small metal ones used by the Indians in the early days of the settling of the West by the Spaniards. They were used as a medium of exchange among the Indians long before the advent of the white man on this continent; when the Indians were in danger and had to flee for their lives they often buried quantities of the crosses which they planned to dig up on their return. Most of the time they did not return and the crosses remained where they were buried, unknown to any living soul.

This woman, however, would "see" their exact location so vividly in her mind that she could lead anyone to them, and over a period of years succeeded in finding many crosses. A sizable collection of them may be seen now on display at the Mission

Inn in Riverside, California, where a narrator relates their story to tourists each day.

She also had "hunches" as to where to find lost money. It was always money which was really lost, with no way of finding the owner in spite of advertising. She would have a vision of a wallet lying in the middle of a well-traveled road, for instance, and invariably when she reached the spot, it would be there. In this way she obtained enough money to make payments on the small bungalow she and her husband occupied. These trips, for both the crosses and the money, were authenticated through her description of the circumstances and location prior to leaving her house for the search for them, in writing and in the presence of reputable and notarized witnesses, with the writing sealed until after the finding of the articles.

Often children show a gift for clairvoyance also. A friend of ours has a four-and-a-half-year-old niece who has shown remarkable ability. She perceives events from a couple of days to two or three weeks before they happen. I remember two outstanding examples:

One day she came to her mother almost in tears, saying, "Oh, I am so sorry for the baby! He fell down . . . I see him on the sidewalk." The mother, thinking she was just prattling, paid little attention to her, but finally showed her there was no baby on the sidewalk, and comforted her as best she could. The little girl had to be taken to the hospital for an operation a few days later, and while she was in the ambulance en route to the hospital, the eighteen-month-old baby on the second floor of their apartment building pushed the screen out of the window and fell to the sidewalk below.

Another time she was in great distress. She said, "That big man tore my doll in two. He is a bad man!" Two weeks later a little neighbor's girl was playing with the niece's rag doll in front of the apartment house when a man attempted to kidnap her. He took hold of the doll and tried to induce the child to follow him into a car at the curb. But she held onto the doll and screamed; the doll came apart in her hands and the man dashed into the car and sped away.

It is difficult for us to account for such premonitions of actual events. They have not as yet happened or been recorded on our "time track." So how do the sensations of sight and sound connected with them reach the sensitive receptors and mind of a little child? Is this a carry-over from the distant past when man relied more upon the perceptiveness of his senses than upon the conscious thought of his brain? Or is this a forerunner of a greater evolvement of the future? We do not know.

What we do know is that we are in truth "fearfully and wonderfully made," and "it doth not yet appear what we shall be."

Feminine Intuition

We feel these abilities are not limited to a few specially gifted souls. We personally know many people who have them to some degree. It goes unrecognized much of the time: they just have a "strong feeling" or a "hunch" which more often than not proves to be right. As they test it repeatedly, they learn to trust it.

We know a woman with a great deal of ability in both clairaudience and clairvoyance, who both "sees" and "hears" things before they happen. She has had these flashes of insight since childhood. Her teachers would slap her hands with a ruler, for if the teacher said, for instance, "Tomorrow Johnnie will read to us about the cow," the child would interrupt, "But teacher, he won't, because he will be at home with a sore throat tomorrow." And sure enough, Johnnie would be!

When the flashes came they were so vivid she would have to express them in spite of consequences. Her teachers and family tried in every way to break her of this habit, but it persisted. Today she still has the ability and every once in a while astonishes her friends with insight into some situation of which she has no knowledge.

A man she knew once said to her, "You know, I just can't seem to ever get $500.00 in the bank all at once; I can make a deal, sell some real estate or get paid on a note, but then another bill comes due and for some reason I am blocked from getting that $500.00 in the bank. I don't even know how much I have in the bank right now." Instantly, she blurted out, "You have $412.00."

The man shifted his cigar to the other corner of his mouth, swallowed a couple of times, then took out his checkbook and balanced his stubs, which he had not done for two weeks. His balance was exactly $412.00!

Her boss says she is constantly "reading" things before they happen. Before a complete message has come through on the teletype she will say, "Oh, that order from so-and-so came through, didn't it?"

Wherever I see such ability at work I sit back with respect; I have reverence for it.

ANOTHER HOMEY EXAMPLE

My wife has considerable intuitional ability that she showed in the episode of the lamps.

We had decided to "revamp" our living room, which entailed selling some furniture and buying other pieces. Our things are Early American and the lamps for the end-tables presented a problem: modern ones would not do and even the replicas of the early period were not right. After bringing home a couple of pairs and taking them back, my wife began calling numbers in the "For Sale" classified ads in the paper. One morning she talked with a woman in the San Fernando Valley and before she hung up I could tell from her satisfied air that she had found her lamps . . . The astounding thing to me was that the owner could not seem to describe her lamps properly. The total description she was able to give was that "the bottoms were kind of a white glass, sort of rough, and the shades were brown with ruffles."

Yet when Eve hung up she said, "I think I have found my lamps." It was a long drive to the Valley and we were very busy so Eve called the following day to see if the husband, who worked near us, would bring them over for us to inspect them. But he was reluctant to be bothered. So I said, "If you want them, Eve, let's go over, but you'd better call first and see if they are still there, hadn't you?" This was a couple of days later. She said, "I know they are still there."

When we arrived the woman had sold most of the other furniture, but the lamps were sitting there, hobnail glass and brass trim, lovely beige shades. It did not take us long to load them into our car. A few nights later a friend dropped in and noticed our acquisition at once. She said, "Eve, where did you find those adorable hobnail Early American lamps? You must have really shopped to match your color scheme so exactly."

One more point: Eve had told me in advance exactly what she wanted to pay for her lamps, and the price the woman quoted her was exactly that price!

I use these homey, or, if you prefer, homely, examples of feminine intuition because these are things we experience daily, and which I am sure you can duplicate in your own lives. Why not put our "E S P" to work for us? It can make life simpler, and much more fun!

Are We Afraid to Admit Our Own E S P?

What attitude should we adopt toward our own E S P abilities? A good friend of ours nursed a feeling of guilt for many years in silence, she tells us, because people around her, not understanding her ability, made her feel she was "queer" when they saw it in action.

When it was pointed out to her that her associates would adopt the interpretation she herself put upon her comments, she began to refer laughingly to it as her "feminine intuition." They soon were marvelling at her ability and envying her a little, too. It was no longer a "psychic ability" to be looked at askance, but an interesting subject of conversation.

The world accepts us at our own evaluation, a good point to remember when we feel embarrassed, guilty or self-conscious. These are breeders of tension that keep our true self from being known and appreciated.

17

Let's Make Our ESP Work for Us

Many people are prone to explain away such events as we are discussing with the term "coincidence." But it goes beyond the realm of chance. We ourselves are convinced there is an ability at work here that is over and above the presently-accepted scope of our faculties.

Eve often gets a quick little glimpse of the immediate future. She will say, "I feel So-and-so is thinking about us." Shortly the telephone will ring and it will be that person. Or she may say, "I just had a flash of So-and-so and I think I should call him." Sure enough the call was timely because the other party was in need of hearing from us, or had been thinking strongly of us and was about to call.

The other day we were driving down Wilshire Boulevard to pay a call. About six blocks before our destination Eve said, "I just 'saw' a flash of a parking space on the street across from where we are going. It is the first space next to the southeast corner of the street and the only one in the block. If this light changes right now, I will get there in time to get it." Sure enough, we pulled into exactly the space she had described to me.

This sort of thing happens too often to be brushed off as accidental. There was no way she could have gained information regarding this parking space through her senses. So we attribute this to E S P.

But there are other events that we prefer to call "Extra Sensitive Perception" because they stem from an observable happening, though not one on the level of the conscious mind. A case in point was the afternoon we called on friends, walking through the nearby park to their home. After spending a couple of hours with them we returned the same way, and when we got home Eve discovered she had lost one of her favorite earrings, a silver reproduction of an old-fashioned telephone. I wanted to go back and look for it but she said, "No, it's almost dark now. We'll go in the morning."

Morning came but she did not have the urge to go and look for it. In the evening all at once she got a strong feeling we should go on the hunt and said, "I want to look along the way we went, in the park."

So we followed the identical route until we got up on our friends' porch ready to ring their doorbell when she said, "It isn't here; there is no use bothering them. It is in the park somewhere." Having seen this "inner knowingness" in operation before, I acquiesced. By this time it was nearly dark, but the street lights were on and we walked along slowly, she scanning every foot of the walk. Near the corner where we had entered the park the day before she suddenly squealed with joy, bent down and picked up the earring. It was lying in the grass at the edge of the walk and its gleam in the street light had caught her eye. Had we looked in the daylight, in all probability we would not have seen it. As always on a Sunday, the park was crowded and hundreds of persons had passed it that day.

Why hadn't she felt the urge to look for it during the day? Why was she so firm in her conviction it wasn't in our friends' home, so firm that she wouldn't even ring their bell, although she was within six inches of it?

As we discussed various aspects of the episode we concluded that this properly should fall in the category of "Extra *Sensitive* Perception" . . . A part of the mind that functions below the level of conscious perception, had noted the sensation created by the earring dropping (either the sight or the hearing sense or possibly both), and had recorded it in the memory. It was never brought to the surface of the mind so it could be linked with the actual thought, "I just dropped an earring." No, the perception lay there unnoticed, probably because her attention was focussed on something else at the time, and was apparently completely forgotten, until some mechanism, that we do not as yet understand, triggered her into the action that resulted in finding the earring.

We believe all the sensations that are constantly being recorded somewhere in the ten billion-or-so cells of our brains, fall into this category. The exact method by which they are connected with the conscious or reasoning part of our mind so we are made aware of them is a mystery that has defied analysis up to this point. But many people are keenly aware of its operation. I want to emphasize the part we can play in bringing this type of information to our own attention. It is important that we recognize this ability in ourselves so we may utilize it for our own benefit.

As we become more observant, it becomes apparent that tension, in the form of emotional turmoil or extreme fatigue, seems to set up barriers between our conscious mind and the reservoir of our "bank of memories"—our subconscious mind. This is why it is so essential to keep ourselves in that state of relaxed alertness we call "organized coordination without tension." This can make everyday living more enjoyable.

". . . FOR WANT OF A NAIL . . ."

We don't believe you have to conserve on Principle, and save it only for the big, important issues of life. We like to see it work in little things as well as big ones, as in this anecdote concerning a lost flower.

I was the speaker at a dinner meeting one evening at the Huntington-Sheraton Hotel in Pasadena. As we entered, one of the ladies on the reception committee pinned a corsage on Eve's dress. She had worn an artificial flower on her coat, and as she said, this made "too many flowers" so she carried the coat over her arm.

After the dinner as we were getting ready to leave she picked up the coat and noticed the flower was missing. She was quiet a minute then said, "I just saw my flower; it is out in the lobby." We walked through the long hall to the lobby and there on a table by the door was the flower. Hundreds of people had passed it, but, like the earring, it was not molested.

Now Eve wants to tell you of the time her mother misplaced an important check. It was a sizable one and she had turned the house upside down looking for it, to no avail. Painstakingly she retraced all her steps since the check came in the mail, but had no recollection of having put it anywhere.

After she had exhausted every conceivable hiding place in the house, she finally sat down, closed her eyes, folded her hands in her lap and rocked back and forth in the old rocker. Suddenly she jumped up and said, "I wonder if it could be in the stove!"

This was many years ago, when the family had one of the round, top-loading stoves. She raised the lid and pulled out the pile of papers dumped there from the waste baskets earlier in the morning. Fortunately it was a warm morning and they had not had the "little fire" to take the chill off the house. For there was the check!

Did she accidentally knock the check into the wastebasket, unnoticed by her conscious mind, yet recorded in the recesses of her subconscious memory bank? Or did the wind blow the check off the desk while she was out of the room, affording no opportunity for the incident to be recorded in her memory? It matters little, really, whether through her extra sensitive perception she was able to re-call the incident from her subconscious, or whether her E S P told her to look in the stove.

The point is that the relaxation that came from sitting down in the rocker and getting mentally and physically still brought her the desired information.

Teach Yourself to "Listen"

Do we take time enough to be still? Can we train ourselves to quiet our turmoil to really listen? Most of us live in a fast-moving world, where a hundred details, the jangle of a telephone or door-bell, demand our attention. But there are ways of snatching the few necessary minutes. No need to do as the prophets and seers of old did, and go off into the desert for days, solitary and fasting, to get our answers. A few minutes a day, to relax in our busy world, will do wonders for us.

Psychometry

Another phase of the fascinating world we call E S P often comes to our attention both in our own experience and that of people we know. This is the ability known as Psychometry. People who have this gift are able to pick up an object and through some means which has eluded scientific explanation also "pick up" flashes of inner vision or feelings about the history of that object. These vary from detailed accounts of happenings in which the object was involved to descriptions of persons who have owned or handled it. However, I have never heard of accurate prophecy of the future in this connection.

The majority of people we know who "psychometrize" are not professionals in the field, but ordinary people . . . housewives, printers, businessmen. They are as puzzled by their power as are the owners of the articles. Asked how they know these things, they shrug their shoulders and say, "I don't know. I only know they are true."

One evening, a man who has had considerable success in accurately describing events through psychometry related the following episode to us. A skeptic wanted to test him. An atmosphere of disbelief sometimes has a dulling effect on the reader's ability, and it happened in this instance. Incidentally, this is one of the factors that makes laboratory research under rigidly controlled conditions so difficult in these areas. E S P does not as yet work with the predictability and consistency of matter, and its workings apparently are dependent on various intangible factors that do not readily lend themselves to scientific analysis and control.

So the reader, whom we will call George, was unable to "get" anything from the stem-winder watch the man handed him. George stood with it in his hand, feeling silly and seeing nothing but a blank. He started to hand it back to the skeptic, when suddenly he drew it back and exclaimed, "Wait a moment! I smell smoke! It is very thick and I feel as if I were choking! I see a small boy, about ten, in a room filled with smoke, with fire on all sides. He is screaming for help. Did this ever happen to you?" The man sheepishly admitted it had, and that he had had this watch, his grandfather's, in his pocket at the time.

Portrait . . . from a Letter

Several years ago before I met her, my wife was living in another state. She made up her mind rather suddenly to move to Los Angeles. She knew no one in the entire area except her son and his wife. Very few people in her circle of acquaintances knew she was in Los Angeles. A few days after moving into her apartment she was astonished to receive a letter, delivered to her there, in strange handwriting. She had told no one in Los Angeles of her address, and since there was no return address on the envelope, she had no clue as to the writer.

But instantly, as she picked it up and looked at it, she got a flash of an elderly woman's face. It was no one she had ever seen, but it was a kind and wise old face and came through very clearly. It was from a friend of a distant cousin in the east. Eve had written her cousin giving the address of the apartment so she could be contacted there. The cousin at once wrote Mrs. R., an old friend, and asked her to look up Eve.

The letter contained an invitation to meet Mrs. R. at church the following Sunday and then join her for lunch. Mrs. R. regretted having no phone, and made no suggestion as to how she might be identified. My wife went to church the following Sunday and stood in the lobby, watching the several hundred people who entered, hoping to see the face she had seen as she picked up the letter. Sure enough, there it was! She approached the older woman, saying, "Are you by chance Mrs. R.?" And Mrs. R. said, "Yes, but how did you know?" And my wife was forced to give the stock answer, "I don't know. I just knew, that's all."

Now, to us there is nothing supernatural or "spooky" about such experiences. We look at them as natural and wholesome.

Although as I have said, psychometry is one of those things that has not been pegged down in a laboratory, there is a theory that seems to explain it as well as any to date. In some way we evidently leave an imprint upon everything we contact—an imprint of our personality, our appearance and our history. The students of psychometry say that a part of us impregnates things we touch, in particular, so that people with a certain sensitivity can pick up these impressions sometimes many years after the contact. Some think that the impressions are imprinted on each individual atom by means of the "vibrations" of the object; others feel that each atom has its own "core of intelligence" that can store them.

I include psychometric ability in our "Extra Sensitive Perception" category because I believe some day we will have a practical explanation of our ability to receive information through this source, and that it may then be considered as an extension of the "feeling" sense we all possess.

AUTOMATIC WRITING

Many phases of man's little-understood capacities are controversial, completely unexplainable and, for the most part, impractical. We will merely touch lightly upon them here. One of these is automatic writing, in which a person writes material he is unfamiliar with, often in a foreign language he has never heard of. The writing may be in longhand or on the typewriter. A young woman we know has written—and published—an entire book purporting to come through a being on another planet. There are many similar publications on the market. The Oahaspe Bible is an example of automatic writing and is read and revered as revelation by thousands.

The commonly accepted theory for automatic writing is that it springs from the writer's subconscious mind. I have not heard a theory to account for one writer who used hieroglyphics for his expression, which could only be translated by a trained Egyptologist.

"TONGUES" AND LONG DISTANCE DIAGNOSIS

Closely related to this ability is that of "speaking in tongues," an ancient phenomenon mentioned several times in the Bible. A person speaking in tongues is usually in a state of consciousness other than the normal conscious state and he will speak or sing in languages not known to himself or to anyone present. In a public demonstration of group hypnosis a woman we knew who was being "regressed" to a former incarnation suddenly broke out into a song in a strange-sounding language. It was a low, sweet melody, and she went through all the motions of a woman rocking her baby in her arms. The hypnotist explained to her we could not understand the words and asked her to translate them into English. As she did, the rhythm and melody were identical to the first song, and the words were clearly understandable. She explained, while still in the "trance state," that she was a gypsy girl who had lived several hundred years ago.

This woman sat in our living room a couple of weeks later and told us she had had the "gift of tongues" since childhood. She could use it at will. She proceeded to demonstrate it, speaking in what appeared to be several different languages, none of which had any resemblance to modern foreign languages. Many times language experts have studied tapes made of such sessions and have found the languages spoken were "dead" languages, not in use today in any part of the world, but distinguishable and capable of being translated.

Thomas A. Sugrue's book *There Is a River* describes in detail the life of Edgar Cayce, the man from Virginia who was able, while in a sleep or trance state, to diagnose and prescribe successfully for illness and disease all over the world. In his normal state of consciousness he had not the slightest knowledge of the medical field. Thousands of case histories left in his files at the

Cayce Center in Virginia Beach, Virginia are currently being studied and catalogued in an attempt to shed more light on his phenomenal ability.

X-RAY OF THE PSYCHE

For centuries certain men and some women have had the ability to "dowse" for water or oil. By holding in their hands a forked twig, such as willow or elm, and walking over terrain they are able to determine the depth of an underground stream of water. Oil and mineral deposits have also been located in this way. I have never seen a "dowser" operate, but have had people tell me of having seen the willow branch turn with such force in the dowser's hands as to loosen the skin from his fingers, as it pointed downward to the underground flow.

In spite of widespread scoffing by unbelievers, there are many thousands who are convinced of the truth of dowsers' claims.

Novelist Kenneth Roberts has written a fascinating book, properly notarized and authenticated, recounting the activities of a New England dowser of renown; the book is *Henry Gross and His Dowsing Rod,* published by Doubleday and Company.

Attempts to explain this particular ability have been mostly unsatisfactory. Many people believe it to be due to a peculiar "affinity" between the subconscious mind of the dowser and the vibrations created by the presence of water (or oil, or minerals) beneath the surface of the earth. This theory collapses in the light of the dowser who, instead of walking over actual terrain, uses a map of a territory, as did Mr. Gross on numerous occasions. His "map dowsing" was authenticated as to its accuracy by subsequent drilling of wells in the unlikely spots he indicated on the map of a distant island.

We are awed by the feats of our modern "electronic brains." The potentials of man's mind are even greater.

18

My Own Experiences with ESP

The methods I am sharing with you in this book are those I used to integrate myself physically, mentally and spiritually as I began to get acquainted with the four-sensed world after losing my sight. As I progressed, everything confirmed my conviction that the better I integrated myself, the more I could add to my awareness of the outside world by developing other skills. I was soon able to tell a lot about a person by the way he walked and conducted himself.

One afternoon, after a busy day answering letters, I said to my wife, "While you are getting dinner I will walk over to the mailbox with these letters." As I approached the corner and turned to cross the first intersection I heard a young woman coming up behind me. As I crossed the street I noticed she increased her speed, telling me she was concerned for my welfare. So I went ahead just to show her I could do it with my eyes shut! Then I waited on the other side for her.

I said to her, "I would like to walk over to the mailbox with you." Immediately she put her arm out to me, saying "Sure! Take ahold!" As we went down the street I said, "Are you wondering why I asked to walk with you?" Without waiting for a reply I went on, "Naturally it is easier. But the real reason is because I could tell by your footsteps you are a friendly, outgoing person . . . someone I would enjoy meeting."

Naturally this pleased her, but I was sincere in my analysis. She said, "Tell me, what made you think of me that way?" I explained that I felt we have ways of communicating with each other on the nonverbal level. I told her how my wife and I communicate, without using words. Not through mental telepathy as such, but often when one of us thinks of something, the other, in less than thirty seconds, will start talking about the same thing.

She admitted this had often happened with her but she had not realized it was such a common occurrence and had not given it much thought. We agreed we should recognize every wonderful capacity we have, whether it is a routine or an occasional experience.

I should be accustomed to it by now, but I am still delighted with the accuracy of the impressions I pick up often on meeting strangers. After one of my lectures to an executive group, the president of the company was introducing me to some of his staff members. One of them said, "You intrigue me, Dr. Corbin. What can you tell me about myself?" I told him if I did not get a strong feeling about a person anything I said would be only a guess. However I would accept his challenge because I felt strongly about him.

I told him his height, his weight and his age and finally said, "You have a good broad forehead and expressive eyes. You are either from the South or are a colored man, I can't tell which and you have been either an educator or a top executive or both." He said, "You amaze me! You really only missed one thing: I am two pounds heavier than you said." It developed that he had been the president of a Negro college a few years back, so he was both an educator and an executive.

One other experience along this line stands out in my memory because I cannot trace the information I received to any sense perception. During my second eastern lecture tour I was standing with the president of the company whose firm I was addressing, meeting some of his executives before the dinner. As one man came up to me I shook hands with him and said, "You are about five feet and sixteen inches tall, aren't you?" He thought a moment and said, "That's right—six foot four!" This pleased the president and he began to ask me for details about each man as he introduced him.

I was in good form that day and it seemed that invariably when I did express my feeling about someone it proved correct. Then the president said, "Here comes a man I want you to meet." I could not hear him approach me on the carpeted floor, and before he spoke or before I shook his hand I had a very strong feeling about him . . . instantaneously the figure "300" came to me. As we shook hands I said, "You are six feet three, aren't you?" He said, "Exactly. How did you know?" Then the president asked me how much he weighed and instead of saying "300," which I thought *must* be wrong, I said "260." He said, "No, you're wrong: 334!"

The Knower within is often more accurate than our logical or reasoning conscious thoughts.

SOME EXPERIENCES WITH COLOR

Although I have been without light perception for many years, I am occasionally pleased to catch a flash of color. Sometimes as I pick up a carrot or a tomato and I raise it to my lips I get a flash of the true color just as vividly as when I had sight. It is only the briefest instant, but nonetheless thrilling to me. Sometimes I get a vague sense of shape, but it is not exact. This also happens with an orange once in a while, and when I first lost my sight I had a bright yellow tie that excited my eyes tremendously.

Eye doctors agree certain stimuli can affect the nerve centers of the brain in a way that approximates the sense of sight. Brain surgeons have been able to induce "flashes of light" in a patient by touching a portion of the exposed brain with the end of a scalpel. It has been proven memory can be evoked under the same circumstances by the same method, that of touching the brain tissue in a certain location. I used to try to rationalize my own flashes of color by attributing them to memory of the objects, but this theory resembles a sieve when I apply it to an instance like the following one.

Very frequently as I enter a room for the first time I will get a flash of the prevailing color scheme; if it is strong enough I often will ask for a verification of my hunch and it is a thrill to find I am right.

One evening Eve and I were attending a gathering at the home of our friend, Gina Cerminara, the author of *Many Mansions* and *The World Within*. We were late in arriving, and the room was filled with people standing around chatting. It was our first visit to Gina's home, and as I stepped into the room I said to Eve, "I feel this room is green and pink. Am I right?" She glanced around and said, "No, Floyd. It is just green . . . the walls and drapes are both green." I had felt the colors so strongly I was surprised to be wrong. A little later she pressed my arm and said, laughing, "You were right and I was wrong! There is a pink rug on the floor, but so many people are standing on it, I hadn't noticed it before."

It is not unusual for me to "feel" the coloring of a girl or woman I am meeting for the first time, and usually when I "feel" it the strongest, her coloring is on the red side. She will have red or auburn hair, perhaps with green eyes, which I also pick up, or is a reddish blond with blue eyes.

These flashes of color give me a link with the outside world I would not otherwise have.

My Built-In "Radar"

Since losing my sight my voyage of self-discovery has led me to many delightful new ports. I can usually tell exactly where I am, geographically speaking. Whether I am on the West Coast, the mid-West or the South, I am very seldom confused about directions. This comes through like an instinct: I don't have to think about it, I merely have to express it. This talent came in handy when my wife was learning her way around ninety-some cities of Southern California while driving me to lectures, many of them night engagements. I also have a sense of distance that is almost infallible.

Repeatedly as we are driving I will say, "Where are we? This feels like the corner of Sepulveda and Wilshire to me" and we won't be twenty feet from that corner. Recently while driving with two other couples to the dock in Wilmington, where one of the couples was to embark for a trip to Honolulu, our driver missed his turn. When we were only a few blocks beyond it I asked him if he was sure of his directions. We all had a good laugh at his expense because he had to turn around to get back on the road leading to the dock.

A San Diego friend often calls me from the outskirts of Los Angeles on his way to make a business call, to ask directions for reaching his destination. One day he picked me up to drive to Bakersfield. As we drove I gave him explicit directions: "Now, we go north here for ten blocks, then we turn left." As we approached our left turn I warned him of it in advance so he could get into the proper lane to make his turn.

I have never felt these were exceptional feats; nature is filled with countless examples of this marvelous ability in other forms of life so we should not think of it as anything miraculous but should be grateful for the Intelligence in man that makes it possible. Although we have evolved far beyond the stage of living on the instinctual level, I believe certain remnants of our instincts remain. They could be of inestimable value to us if we would learn to recognize and use them as do birds and animals.

Certain species of birds return from many thousands of miles, year after year, to their nesting grounds. Baby salmon swim far out to sea but return to spawn to the exact stream where they were born.

I try to keep my built-in "radar" system in good working order by using it constantly.

How Do We "Sense" Time?

I have never used a Braille watch, because I have never felt the need for one. I can tell the passage of time quite accurately with my "built-in alarm clock." Several times a day I will think of whatever hour seems right to me, and on checking with Eve or dialing the telephone to verify it, find I am seldom off more than a few minutes. I never depend on this sense to awaken me in the morning for an important appointment, however, even though I share with many people the ability to awaken at a set hour. I believe this common experience is based on telling oneself emphatically the night before the hour one wishes to awaken, and this prevents me from having sound, restful sleep. So I don't mind substituting a mechanical alarm clock for my E S P under those conditions.

Often just previous to one of my lectures, the program chairman, who is always under some tension for fear he has drawn a long-winded speaker, will say, "Shall I let you know when your time is up?" I always tell him, "If you don't feel I am ready to close within a minute of the time you have set for me, then you may pull my coattail." I seldom miss it.

Masculine Intuition

I don't know whether men can equal women in being consistently intuitional, but we do have flashes of this inner "knowing" and should learn to heed them.

We were driving to a near-by town for a lecture when a man's name flashed through my mind. (Observe that these bits of insight come quickly and pass as quickly; we have to learn by experience to recognize them and to seize upon them at once, or they will evaporate.) I said, "Pull up at the next phone booth; I have to make a call." My wife complied and I called the man at his office. When I explained the reason for my call he said, "You don't know how timely this is: I am due at a board meeting in fifteen minutes to discuss plans for our Ladies Night program and we are in need of a speaker for it." I drove to his office, left him a brochure and as a result was engaged for the occasion.

A minister friend and his wife dropped in one evening and asked me to speak at the Wednesday night service on a certain date. Instead of accepting it, although the date was open at the time, I said, "How about later on in the month? I believe it would be better for me." He agreed, and we set up the date for the last Wednesday.

A couple of days later while writing letters I suddenly had an urge to call a man I hadn't thought of for months. I did so and as I reminded him of my identity he said, "Now, isn't this something? For the last hour I have been trying to locate your brochure in my files but couldn't find it. I wanted you to speak to my sales group. Are you busy on such and such a night?"

The night he asked for was the night I had turned down for my minister friend because Something had said to me, "Keep it open."

OUR DREAMS—CAN WE TRUST THEM?

Although we have been talking about E S P for some time, we still have not defined it. Many people are hazy about the term and I like to give them this definition: "Extra Sensory Perception, or E S P, as it is commonly called, is the acquisition of specific authentic information by a means other than that furnished by any of the five senses."

Thousands of cases are on record in which people have received information which is later verified, without the use of any of their ordinary senses. One of the commonest of these experiences involves dreams. Everyone has had odd dreams, dreams which make him wonder, dreams which make him fearful. The study of dream analysis by psychologists and psychoanalysts has contributed many interesting theories. I only want to share one of my own experiences with you to point up some of my own ideas about dreams.

My mother, for many years, seemed to be informed through her dreams of any significant change that took place in her sons' lives. This used to annoy me no end, especially after I had left home. Like every normal boy I liked to believe I was entirely on my own. But if something unusual had taken place in my life, shortly there would be a letter from Mother saying she had had a dream, and she knew something had taken place. It seemed her dreams were accurate regardless of whether the change was good or bad.

As I began to mature I looked on this phenomenon in a different light. Instead of resenting it I began to appreciate it, but still could not understand it. As I grew older and had a family of my own I began to realize this ability was mine, too.

One night I was awakened out of a sound sleep by my daughter-in-law's voice saying to me, "Dad, they have just taken your son to the hospital with a heart attack." Not only did I hear her voice clearly, I saw her face and hair, framed in a golden light, six inches or so over and above my right eye. At this time I was completely without sight yet her face was as sharp as if I saw it, and the voice as clear as if she were in the room.

By now I had had enough experience with dreams not to panic. But I was curious and dialed the telephone by my bed for the time: it was just 1:04 A.M. Then I went back to sleep, promising myself I would check up on it first thing in the morning.

I called their home around seven o'clock. My daughter-in-law answered the phone. I said, "How are you kids this morning?" and she replied, "Not too good, Dad. We had kind of a rugged night." She went on, "My Dad had a heart attack during the night and they called us to take him to the hospital." I said, "I'm sorry to hear that. What time did they call you?" she answered, "One o'clock."

The message that something was wrong came through to me only four minutes late . . . However, the message was not completely accurate! It was her father, not my son, who had the heart attack.

Check these flashes of insight to make sure they are absolutely correct *before* reacting to them.

My Own "#1" E S P Experience

The following events still remain as vivid in my mind, after several years, as the morning they happened.

It is my habit to awaken at dawn. By the time the first bird chirps once and brushes his feathers down twice, I am awake and either on my way out for a walk, or reading from my Talking Book Machine. A Talking Book Machine is a record player; the Library of Congress supplies books read onto records to those people with ten per cent vision or less, who then "read" the books by playing the records. Much literature is thus made available to those without sight. *The Reader's Digest,* travelogues, biographies, books on science, poetry, fiction and a vast range of other subjects are available, and I count my Talking Book Records one of my greatest blessings. (Your nearest Braille library can supply additional details if you wish them.)

This particular morning I had awakened as usual, and turned on a record before getting up. It had just finished playing one side and I sat up on the edge of the bed to turn the record. As I placed my feet on the floor I was facing due east.

I reached for the record, turning to the right, which was south and just as I did there was a strange noise, something like a small creaking sound. At the same time I felt a flood of warm light strike the back of my neck and the left side of my face. By this time I had developed facial vision so I was sensitive to heat on my face, such as the rays of the sun. I turned instantly to face the light, that was as if a crew of photographers had come through the door somehow without opening it, and had turned on a battery of floodlights simultaneously.

As I turned toward the door exactly due north, I saw a golden light streaming through the door, especially intense as it came from the top part of the door. It was as warm as the morning sun breaking over the hill. Then there was a terrific flash of light. For some reason I looked again toward the south.

Two large windows with Venetian blinds were wide open and through them I saw the entire countryside lit up. As my apartment was on the sixth floor of a hotel I could see several miles to the south: the countryside looked exactly as I had remembered seeing California in previous visits. Not only did I see the Venetian blinds and the buildings through them, but also the complete appearance of the room . . . the green corduroy upholstery, green rugs and walls, blond furniture, rose-colored lamps and drapes, the desk and its chair, an ivy plant in the planter on the wall . . . all was exactly as I had imagined and had been told it was. Then it was gone. All was dark again.

Now the building began to sway and rock. I picked up the phone and called the desk clerk. I said, "They finally got us, didn't they?" He said, "What do you mean, 'got us'?" I said, "The Russians dropped a bomb, didn't they?" unconsciously basing my opinion on the great flash of light and the swaying of the building. "No," he said, "it was an earthquake, I guess." Being on the sixth floor we got nearly an eighteen-inch sway, and when the studio bed quit swinging I collected myself. I had been in earthquakes before, but the combination of the golden light and the sway had apparently kept me from linking it with a quake.

I was thoroughly puzzled by the whole experience, particularly the part of it involving my few seconds of sight. I have since talked to professors at the University of Southern California and at the University of California in Los Angeles about it, but no one, including their scientists, ever had any valid explanation.

MY GOLDEN LIGHT

That night a client dropped in, a young man in his early twenties who was badly disturbed about an experience that had cost him his job. After we had discussed his problem and he had read several different passages in books I had suggested, he left. Shortly afterwards I discovered he had left the books lying on the davenport. As I reached to pick them up, there was that strong golden light in my face again.

Remember, I had no light perception, yet there was light, warm and bright and golden. I experimented with it, moving back or leaning to left or right and found it would disappear then. But each time I leaned over I would run into it again.

It startled me, but eventually in spite of it I picked up the books and replaced them on the bookshelf in back of the davenport. In the following days we continued to have earth-tremors and each time the room would light up for me, though not to the extent that I could actually see. Whenever I would bend over to pick up something, or over the washbasin, the light appeared again. By now I had lost all fear of it. But it was annoying and I made up my mind to investigate.

Finally one day I concluded I had the answer. It seemed that whenever my shirt was open at the neck and I bent over, the light would invariably appear. I concluded that the heat from my body, coming up through my open collar, struck my neck and face, already sensitized to facial vision, and that this stimulated the nerve centers to conduct an impulse to my brain, which in turn interpreted it as seeing light. So I rejoiced in my discovery. Experimenting further I discovered that when my shirt was buttoned I no longer experienced the light. Happily I felt the light would never bother me again.

However a few weeks later, when my shirt was buttoned, my tie on and no heat about, there was the light again. It continued to appear periodically until that Saturday night. I sat in the solitude of my room, and prayed that the Intelligence within me would show me how to cope with this annoying and persistent phenomenon. After I finished I felt better.

The next morning I went to church and heard one of my favorite speakers, Dr. Fredrick Bailes, a nationally known lecturer and author of several books, among them the best-seller, *Hidden Power for Human Problems.* In the course of his talk Dr. Bailes said, in effect, that numbers of people were beginning to have clairvoyant and psychical experiences, and that as we continue to grow and to expand our scope of awareness, more and more people will have them. He said that although we cannot account for many of these things with the knowledge we have right now, the best way to handle them was to bless them when they happened: simply to say, "I don't know just what you are or your purpose, and I do wish you well, but please go away and leave me now. I bless you!"

So I went home and did this. The light disappeared for good and I have never been bothered with it since. I have never accounted for it. I have just chalked it up along with all the other baffling events as part of our "E S P".

SUMMING IT UP

In this book we have thought together about a variety of phenomena, and have agreed that although they are not new on the human scene, neither are they explainable by the usual methods of logic, reasoning or science.

Man is a curious animal, always asking "Why?" and "How?" You may wonder if I ever found an explanation for the lovely golden flood of light I saw. Here is the only one I have found that made any sense to me.

It is conceded that the core of the earth is a molten mass of matter. When there is a quake of sufficient intensity it is possible the core is stirred enough for it to emit radiations of some sort, although they are not visible to the naked eye. According to the seismographs, the quake centered south of Bakersfield, which is north of Los Angeles, and I saw the light coming from the north door of the apartment. These rays no doubt travel faster than the speed of sound and faster than the motion of the shaking earth. It seems I must have seen them thirty seconds before the quake, but it was probably more like ten. There was a grill at the top of my door which would permit the rays to enter more easily and with more intensity than through the solid part of the door.

When the rays struck, my face, highly sensitized, felt them; this sensation was transferred to the cells of my brain, where it acted as a stimulus to activate my "seeing center" there. Whether I saw through my eyes, or around them or without their aid, I do not know, but it did enable me to actually perceive the furnishings of my apartment and the scene through the Venetian blinds. This theory, of course, does not account for the slight creaking noise that preceded the light, and which attracted my attention to it first. But then, what theory fulfills all details of a premise?

Such experiences encourage me to believe that as man continues to grow and to develop his native and innate capacities, as he continues to improve on methods of integrating his whole organism to insure his operation as a unified though still triune being of body, mind and spirit, he will have increasing numbers of such experiences.

I, for one, will continue to bless every constructive experience that links man and the Infinite. I know, too, that every effort we make to free ourselves of our self-inflicted tensions and strains also frees us to see and hear more clearly those sights and sounds that "eye hath not seen and ear hath not heard."

Mud, Magic and Miracles!

"Two men look out through prison bars: one sees mud, the other, stars!"

It is possible that a man's work, by which he earns his livelihood, is the most important single segment of his life. His innermost conviction regarding the dignity of his job and its place in the general scheme of life, is what makes him "tick." His working conditions may not be ideal, but if he feels basically right about his job, he can lift himself out of the subservient category and maintain his self-respect.

Three men were working on a generator in a power plant. Asked what they were doing, the first said, "I am earning $25.00 a day." The second said he was working on a generator. The third man said he was lighting a city. It is only by focusing his attention upon the higher aspects of his job and identifying with them that man can rise above the drudgery, petty annoyances and the continual postponement of his dreams. The man who keeps his nose to the grindstone too persistently is likely to see only mud, or at best the water as it drips over the wheel. The person who wants to get ahead and to discover and expand his

153

true self must take time to lift his eyes while turning the grind-
stone, to enlarge his perspective of life.

IMAGERY—A MAGIC WAND?

Today we hear many success "recipes." Teachers, classes,
records, courses . . . nearly everyone wants to tell you "how
to succeed"! Methods range from "success imagery" to sleep
teaching and hypnotism, *ad infinitum*. But the principle behind
most of them is the same one man has used for centuries. One of
its basic steps is imagery. "What man can conceive, man can do."
"If you have the mental equivalent, you can have IT!" In this
book I have often used the phrase, "Sit down and think about
and ponder upon it, until . . ." because we know that every job,
every business, every bridge ever built, every accomplishment
of man, had its origin in the quiet, private world of thought in
which we all dwell.

REHEARSAL FOR A "PLUS" PERFORMANCE

It has been demonstrated under controlled conditions that
deliberate mental imagery, done before actual performance,
paves the way to success. It is logical that it should work this way
since it conditions the person's mental attitude and actually gives
preliminary practice of sorts. It is a pity so few people are aware
of it or utilize it in their own lives.

Experiments have been made with this "dry run" technique,
in which a group of boys was divided into two teams. One team
was first instructed to sit down and imagine themselves throwing
darts and hitting the bull's-eye. The other group was given no
instruction but was put into the game in competition with the
other group immediately. The "dry run" boys showed a consistently higher score in every test.

The man who sits down and thinks out his next day's calls
on his customers, going through every detail, even to shaking
hands with a customer and finally going out the door with his
order, can improve his income as much as 100%, providing he

does this consistently over a period of time. The storekeeper whose business has hit a slump can use imagery by seeing customers pouring into his store, picturing himself turning them into permanent satisfied customers.

If the inexperienced hostess who yearns to have a really successful dinner party will "pay attention" to it ahead of time, outlining every detail mentally from the time she greets her guests until she closes the door on the last one, she will be delighted with the smoothness of her evening. This has nothing to do with the mechanical preparations of the dinner, which she must also work out beforehand. But by her preliminary "rehearsal" of the evening she herself will be free of tensions because she will feel at home in her role. There will be no confusion, no lost motion, no awkward moments. She will face her dinner party with confidence.

This simple technique will always work if properly applied, which makes it a principle rather than merely a useful piece of advice. Most successful persons use it routinely, I am sure: the pianist, before a recital, to bring poise and confidence, the attorney, "living through" his next court trial. Public speakers are especially fond of the "dry run" technique and I want to illustrate it with a personal example.

One night my telephone rang and a friend said, "Floyd, we just got word that one of our speakers can't keep his appointment to speak before our Toastmaster's group. Could you fill in for us if I picked you up in the next five minutes?"

This was early in my Toastmastering days and in my rehabilitation as well. My first impulse was to say, "No. I haven't anything prepared." But Something in me suggested, "Wait a moment: you are always talking about taking Life's hand when it is extended to you: this is an opportunity for you to practice what you preach." So I agreed.

Then I sat down in my favorite chair and pictured myself standing before the group. I saw myself poised, calm and confident, speaking with sincerity and an easy flow that held their attention and drew their laughs. I not only *saw* myself doing it, I *felt* myself doing it. I felt the vibration of their applause as I finished. Then I saw myself called up to accept the Cup for the best speech of the evening. I went through every detail of the next few hours.

By this time my friend called for me. As we drove to the meeting I outlined mentally some of the high points of my speech, as well as my opening and closing remarks. This was at a time when I was consciously cultivating the spiritual approach to everything in my life, so now I took a minute to add, "It is not I, but the Father within me that doeth the works." Then I dismissed the speech from my mind and talked with my friend until we arrived at the hall.

I found I was to be one of four speakers competing for the Cup. One man had already been selected to represent the club at the Area Speak-Off; he was practicing his speech for that occasion tonight. I was second on the program and when I got up to speak it was as if I were going through a play I had rehearsed. I did not falter; my ideas and words flowed fluently. As I sat down I was confident I had the Cup for that night. So it was no surprise when the judges awarded it to me: I had won it, an hour before, in my imagination!

Can imagery be used as a kind of magic to insure success? Yes, it will help tremendously. But it should be used only as an adjunct, a complementary tool while we are acquiring all the information, knowledge, skill and art to bear upon the subject. We must "pay the price" of work, application, study and practice. It is then that the "dry run" technique pays off best.

ARE WE ADVANCING?

As primitive man's intelligence developed and he began to influence his environment to meet his needs, he used imagery extensively. It is thought this is the principle of the cave paintings of early man found in certain regions of France. Hunting was the crux of his life, since life itself depended upon his skill in bringing down wild animals for food, clothing and even for weapons which he made from horns, tusks and bones.

The cave paintings, almost without exception, depict hunting scenes in which huge animals are pictured transfixed with spears and darts. To the painter's elemental mind, it seemed that if he could picture the game as wounded and slain, this would be a powerful factor in the success of the hunter. Man himself is seldom pictured, and then always with a mask over his face, presumably with the idea that this made the hunter invisible to his prey.

Many tribes have practiced drawing or forming an image of a fish and putting it in the water, headed in the direction from which they expected schools of fish to come, thinking this would influence their catch. It is but a step from this concept to the well known practice of "black magic" or voodoo, in which an image of a person who is to be the subject of the death wish is formed, then stuck with pins or darts at vital points. The belief in such "magic" and its practice is one of the powerful holds that the religions of backward peoples have on their followers. The "medicine man" in one form or another will probably continue to flourish as long as people are uninformed, unenlightened and spiritually too lethargic to attempt to develop their own abilities.

When they lack authentic knowledge about a situation that involves their life or safety, many people resort to superstition or ritual in which they have confidence. They rely on these things to alleviate their fear and anxiety.

HORSESHOES, CATFISH AND OUIJA BOARDS

In the attempt to ease their fears about death or the hereafter they search for many explanations. Sometimes these involve attributing power to idols, masters and guides, spirits of the dead and certain ritualistic acts to fend off danger. This leaning toward mystical or magic elements involves widespread reliance on good-luck charms, rabbit's feet, four-leaf clovers, horseshoes and the like. I have known people who would not start a trip on Friday, nor sleep in a hotel room numbered thirteen, nor walk under a ladder. These are the same ones who reach to "rap on wood" when speaking of a misfortune.

Even in today's enlightenment we were surprised to overhear a conversation in which a woman told a friend she must remind herself to buy salt for a friend who was moving . . . "You know, it is supposed to be bad luck to take old salt into a new home!" She laughed as she said it, but nevertheless it was evident she intended to buy that salt!

For centuries the Japanese had a legend to explain their frequent earthquakes. They said that the island of Japan rested on the back of a giant catfish and when it played, the earth shook. After an earthquake, you might hear a native say, "The catfish played hard last night," gesturing with his hand to show the fish swimming playfully.

Even the Birds Are Not Immune!

An amusing example of how even the lower species will rely on a kind of "magic"—that of irrelevant motions—to gain their ends is told in an experiment with pigeons. Researchers into the habit-formation patterns of birds had devised an apparatus for feeding pigeons in a cage. When the birds pushed a certain lever with their bills a bell rang and wheat dropped through a slot. After they had been thoroughly conditioned to this sequence through suitable repetitions, the apparatus was changed so that the wheat dropped only every third or fourth time.

Much to the amazement of the experimenters, one of the pigeons would stand on one foot after pushing the lever, and would not move from it until the wheat was released. They had certainly not taught him this, but somewhere in the recesses of his bird-mind he was disappointed when no wheat was forthcoming; the next time he pushed it, he had stood on one foot for a moment and just then the wheat was released. He must have been a smart pigeon and very easily conditioned, for from that time on you could never have convinced him that standing on one foot did not influence the delivery of the wheat.

A Warning from "George"

In the realm of the supernatural and its hold on some people, I once had a vivid example of how completely a person may be influenced by his beliefs. One night when I came into the hotel where I was living the switchboard operator told me a woman had called me three or four times during the evening and left a message that I was to call her regardless of the hour I came in.

When I did so, she told me she had just received a message on her ouija board that the hotel in which I was living was going to be destroyed by a violent storm the following Saturday night. She insisted I pay attention to this warning and asked me to promise that I would not remain in the hotel. When I questioned her about the source of the message on the ouija board she said it came from a deceased uncle by the name of George who was her guide or "canopy" and who had been directing her activities for the past few weeks.

I didn't promise her I would leave and neither did I offend her by ridiculing her prediction, for she seemed sincere. However, I put her off without committing myself and proceeded to forget the matter. The following Saturday she called me early in the afternoon, reminding me the time was getting short. Late that evening I had another call from her. This time I had only an hour left! I promised to call her back in a few minutes, then made two or three telephone calls and verified the fact that the weather report predicted fair and warmer for the next five days. Then I went to bed.

As the hour for the predicted storm approached this woman almost collapsed under the anxiety. When the hour had passed and she knew the hotel was still intact, she finally did collapse. You see, the turmoil and storm were in her own mind and she had permitted herself to place her belief in the ouija board without taking time to develop a few facts. We often find that people have a tendency to reach for and substitute the "fringe area" for good common sense. Remember this incident the next time you are under tension and tempted to listen to the superstitious.

Do We Depend on "Miracles"?

Too many times in our modern civilization people, like the gullible pigeon, "stand on one foot" hoping substance will drop in their laps.

A man I knew, a realtor, had taken a thousand dollars as a deposit on a piece of property. Instead of holding this money in escrow, he had used it to buy an option on another piece of property which he felt sure he could sell in a matter of days, thus making himself a tidy profit. However, he was not able to follow through; nor did the deal go through on the property for which he had received the thousand dollar deposit.

As a result, the contractor who had paid the deposit insisted on the return of his money, according to their agreement. The realtor had stalled him so long that the contractor finally threatened him with a suit. The realtor had exhausted every possible avenue of raising the money. He was desperate. In his extremity he did as many persons do—he turned to religious counseling for help. He demanded that his counselor pray that he receive a thousand dollars by the next morning, even if it had to come "direct from heaven."

Fortunately for him the person whose help he sought was a realistic as well as an ethical man, and he said, "I would not think of praying in that manner—for a miracle to extricate you from the results of your own wrongdoing. But I will pray that you will be guided into right action in the best way to handle this situation with benefit to all concerned."

The realtor was disappointed, but not knowing what else to do, went home and to bed. When he awakened it was with the strong urge to go and see the contractor, make a clear confession of exactly what he had done and throw himself on the man's mercy. He did just that. The contractor, instead of berating him, said, "Why didn't you come to me before? I knew inwardly you must have done something like this. How did I know? Because many years ago, as a young fellow, I did something similar. It taught me a lesson I have never forgotten. In fact, that lesson is probably responsible for my success today.

"I am going to help you take this experience and turn it into an asset, instead of being defeated by it. I want you to make this the turning point of your life and resolve that from this point on, all your business dealings will be forthright and honest. Oh— about the thousand dollars? Give me a note for it and pay it off as you can. But I warn you, if you don't start paying it off in a reasonable time, or if you don't mend your ways of doing business, I won't hesitate to take legal action against you."

The realtor learned his lesson. It changed his life.

How fortunate for him that the counselor had prayed for right action, rather than trying to wave a "magic wand" that might have allowed him to go on repeating such incidents until they became a life pattern.

21

Pay Attention, or Pay —
with Tension!

We are to a great extent the product of our environment.

A group of scientists were exploring the wilds of a sparsely inhabited area of South America, searching for remnants of an ancient Indian tribe reported in existence. They came upon evidences that the tribe was living there but they fled whenever the explorers approached. One day the scientists were so close to the tribe that they found a two-year-old girl left behind by the Indians in their flight. The child was naked and dirty, with matted hair and wild eyes; she was close to starvation and paralyzed with fear.

They could not bring themselves to abandon her, for the tribe might not return for her. So the head of the party assumed responsibility for her. When he returned to his native France he took her with him and made her part of his own family. She was brought up with all the advantages of a well-to-do, highly intelligent French family. Early in life she showed signs of a remarkably keen mind. She was given a fine education and eventually she chose to go back to her native country, where she is now a famous scientist, working tirelessly for the advancement of her own people.

Had this girl remained with her native tribe none of this could have happened. She would have remained an illiterate savage.

Anthropologists tell us one of the basic differences between man and animal is that man has the creative ability to change his environment in order to adapt it to his needs. This is superior to the power of adaptation to environment, which the animal has. If the animal tries to adjust to an inimical environment and fails, he perishes: he lacks the power and ability to actually change his environment other than by his instinctive urges to flee or migrate.

Man has also been able to change animals for the better. Through cross breeding and genetics cattle raisers have succeeded in developing strains of stock with thicker hides to withstand the rigors of extremely cold climates. Wide research in various nutritional factors has improved animals' resistance to disease, aided their growth rate and shortened the period preceding maturity.

Farmers and poultry raisers have long been familiar with the "peck system" among chickens. In every flock there will be one hen who dominates the rest: she will peck at them until they submit to her wishes. Just below her is a hen who can dominate the ones under *her,* and so on down the line. But the last hen has no one left to dominate. Should she resist domination at any time, all the others will peck at her, sometimes until she succumbs. Experimenters keeping records of egg production found that the "last hen" did not lay nearly as many eggs as the more aggressive ones at the top. When they isolated her, giving her a peaceful environment with all the pressure off, to their surprise they found her egg production increased by thirty-three per cent.

Research with milk cows proved that these placid animals are sensitive to their surroundings, too. When all was peaceful and quiet, in keeping with the cows' own natures, they produced considerably more milk than when they were subjected to noise, hurry and stress of any kind. When cows were put in dry, well-lighted stalls with soothing music piped in to them, milk production soared.

How can we benefit from these examples? The ancient Greeks were interested in the effect man's surroundings has on him. They thoroughly explored man's relationship to his *whole* environment: this study was called "ecology." Literally, it means "the study of the whole house." If you are nervous, jittery, easily upset—in other words, if you are a tense person, has it occurred to you the cause might lie in your environment? This is not advising you to look for a place to put all the blame for your tense condition, but there may be contributing factors in your everyday situations. Let's examine some; if none of yours are listed, keep on looking! You may find clues!

RESEARCHING YOUR ECOLOGY

A good place to start is to check your working conditions for sources of physical strain. If you work at a desk, is it so placed that you face a strong light instead of having the light fall on your work? Continued eye strain caused by glare can injure the delicate eye tissues, with resulting eye tension and headaches. A friend complained of continual pain and tightness through her back and shoulder muscles. A little investigation showed her desk to be in direct line with the flow of cold air from the air-conditioner. The result was just enough to tighten her muscles. Her problem was easily solved by moving her desk.

Are you often depressed at meal time? Especially when you eat at home? Perhaps your dining room is dark and dingy, or the view of the brick wall opposite the window is uninspiring, or perhaps fifteen years of eating in the same spot has finally become more than you can take! Shock the neighbors some day by eating your lunch or dinner on television tables on the front porch or lawn. Or put your food in a picnic basket and carry it to the nearest park.

Are you postponing that medical check-up you should have, because, like most men, you hate to visit a doctor? If the little Voice within warns you something is wrong, make an appointment, get down to the office and get an expert's advice on what is bothering you. Many a person fears to hear a verdict of an incurable disease, but a check-up usually reveals some simple thing that yields readily to proper treatment. Decision and action are marvelous antidotes for tension!

Outside Pressures

Nothing can make you more tense than a financial "squeeze." Analyze your living standards; ask yourself, "Am I adhering to an unrealistic standard of living, one that does not jibe with my income, because I feel I must keep up with neighbors or relatives?" Maybe all you need is to take this pressure off. A good rule to follow is, "If you can't live within your income, don't try to live within your credit." Strict budgets are somewhat out of date, but for just a month keep track of every expenditure. You may hit upon a way of decreasing some of your tensions!

Do you feel there are too many demands on your resources? Do you have a sense of "over-load," financially, physically or mentally? Read the "Three Magic Rules" again and make sure you are applying all three to your own situation. Perhaps you need to use the Iron Rule for a change, and suggest to those relatives who moved in with you a few weeks ago, they had better get busy and find a place of their own. This kind of situation has a devastating chain-reaction and is guaranteed to produce tension!

Are you trying to keep up an immaculate yard and lawn because everyone else in your block does, in spite of your inadequate physical energy to do the work? Visit a nursery and investigate plantings and ground covers that require a minimum of care. Replant your yard with them and then give some attention to building up your physical reserves.

Traffic and Time Clocks

A sizable percentage of us live in cities and have jobs. Thus two of the factors in our environment that cause tension are time schedules and transportation. I want to tell you how one young woman solved both of these problems.

Within two minutes after we were introduced at a dinner one evening she told me that she lived in a suburb and drove to downtown Los Angeles every day to her office job. She said she got up every morning dreading her drive on the freeway. She did not enjoy driving under any conditions, so the pressure grew. By the time she reached the office she needed two cups of coffee and a cigarette to "quiet her nerves."

I asked her if she had ever tried to break down the reasons for her nervousness and deal with each one separately. She said the foremost reason was the number of cars on the freeway. "Just think," she said, her eyes round with horror at the thought, "they say there are *fifty thousand cars* on just that one freeway every morning!" I answered, "Well, you need not be concerned with all fifty thousand at once. You need think about only three or four at any given moment: the one behind you, the one in front of you and the one or two beside you. Of course, as a good driver you are watching the flow of traffic all around you, but your immediate concern is only with the cars nearest you. This would be the case on any highway."

This was a completely new idea to her. I could feel her mentally adjusting her worries from the fifty thousand point down to the four. Some of the tension went out of her voice; however it came back as she said, "But they change lanes so fast, and the traffic is so noisy!"

Now, what was really bothering this girl was a combination of many things. She had never adjusted her country driving habits to those of the city. There are some things in life which "just are," and we might as well make up our minds to face up to them. In her case freeway traffic was one of them. However, there were other factors which she *could* control, because they lay in her power. One was her resentment at having to work at all. She really wanted to stay home and keep house; she was afraid her old vintage car would decide to stop for good—on the freeway! She was always under pressure to get to work on schedule. There never seemed to be time to get herself organized for the day.

Let's see what this young mother did about her tensions. First she learned to accept freeway traffic as one of those "unchangeable conditions" and to stop resenting it. She faced up to the necessity of working, at least for a time, since it contributed to a long range goal she was determined to reach: laying up a fund for her children's college education. By merely changing her attitude about these things she was able to control them better. Then she changed some of her habits. She went to bed earlier, which helped her to get up rested, earlier in the morning. She could prepare herself, mentally and physically, for the day, and this included an adequate and leisurely breakfast. She had the car repaired and this gave her additional peace of mind. The last I heard, she had a new job, closer to home.

Operating on a split-second schedule may be necessary in emergencies, but a steady diet of it is a most frustrating experience. Unless you expect the unexpected you will continue to be upset by it when it happens . . . the flat tire, the dead battery, the long-winded customer, the telephone ringing as you go out the door. . . .

Promptness is a state of mind. Setting your mental sail toward the port of punctuality will probably do more good than all mechanical planning. Try another Science of Happiness thought-directive; say, "I am always in the right place at the right time." Remember! Repeat it many times a day always seeing yourself in command and on time. This contributes to success and will help keep the wheels of achievement oiled.

ATTENTION TO EDUCATION PAYS

Many people might think that the happiest person in the world is the Western Union boy with change for a $5.00 bill in his pocket. Their mental picture of this boy is that of a carefree, irresponsible kid who has something to do that taxes neither his mentality nor his physical stamina. Also, he gets to wear a snappy uniform, which gives him a feeling of importance!

This picture may look pleasant until we look behind the scenes. As long as he remains a happy-go-lucky adolescent, with no particular goal beyond a good time next Saturday night, his problems (and his tensions!) are few. But common sense tells us that if, instead of a boy, he is a man with a family he is not likely to be as happy as the man with a better position and higher income. Statistics tell us that the latter is happier, lives longer, enjoys better health and has more freedom. A person's education is one of the determining factors in his environment.

Of course a good income, in itself, does not insure a "better" life. But the man who has paid attention to preparation for his career enjoys a proportionate prestige. He also has the additional income that makes it possible for his family to experience a freedom of expression and a happiness not otherwise attainable.

In the history of our nation many a man with less than an eighth grade education has risen to success. However, with our present technological advancement and our high degree of specialization, the boy or girl without a college education is severely handicapped. This is particularly true of the boy since he is the main wage earner and carries the responsibility of building a career. Ask any eighteen-year-old boy if he would like to earn at least $25,000 a year for the next four years. You know his response. Yet it is possible this boy has not been made to realize that four years in college can be worth at least $25,000 a year to him. Statistics show the college graduate on an average earns from one to two hundred thousand dollars more in a lifetime than the noncollege man. As parents, are you pointing out this advantage to your son?

As for a girl, it is quite possible the most important and productive four years of her life are those spent in college. Again statistics have proven the greater stability of marriages which are founded on a similarity of intelligence, culture, religion and general background, as compared to those where there is a wide discrepancy in these factors. The college woman is in a better position to meet and marry a man of higher educational caliber and with a higher earning potential than the noncollege woman. Certainly what she learns in four years of college if well applied, will be of great help to her in establishing a good home, rearing a fine family, and being a good mate to her husband, as well as a valuable member of her community.

I am not advocating that girls go to college for the sole purpose of finding the mate with the highest earning capacity. But it is a preparation to fill the role of wife, mate and mother which, even in our business-centered way of life, remains a vital part of a woman's existence.

DOES FREEDOM FROM RESPONSIBILITY BRING FREEDOM FROM TENSION?

Occasionally we go to a near-by eating place and have lunch at the outdoor tables. Recently we could not help overhearing the conversation of two women at the next table.

The quiet one was enjoying her lunch. But her talkative companion was not impressed with such a commonplace experience. Her monologue consisted of enumerating the times she and her husband go out for dinner in sophisticated restaurants, and the fact she is free to go out for lunch any time she wants to. This, she informed her companion, is a wonderful way to kill time: "By the time you have a nice long lunch, browse through Bullock's and Magnin's and get home, it is four o'clock and your afternoon is gone, my dear!"

Following this she dwelt at length on the number of her friends with gorgeous homes and swimming pools where they were frequent guests. The next topic was her operations and illnesses, of which she had had "more than her share." We could only hope her afternoon had been satisfactorily "killed" by the time she left to finish her shopping down the boulevard.

This woman's lack of purpose and goal was so obvious we had only compassion for her. We could feel her insecurity and anxiety, and her intense desire to identify herself with a way of life obviously not shared by her friend. Her conversation had been punctuated by revealing phrases, such as, "Oh, I never read . . . I don't have time!" and the vague, "You know what I mean . . ."

The episode reminded me of the way our car had been acting the past few days. The mechanic at the garage said it had a "miss" in the motor; this caused it to chug and shake while it was idling or driven slowly. When we drove at normal speed it sailed along and carried us to our destination with no trouble. Our mechanic friend told us the trouble was probably due either to a faulty valve or a dirty carburetor, and said it would run smoothly as we gained momentum, but would "shake and jiggle" when the motor was idling.

When our inner "motor of Life" is idling—when we have no worthwhile goal to give purpose to our days, we too will go through a lot of motions without getting anywhere. When we are actually idle complications seem to set in: feelings of depression, anxiety, frustration and dissatisfaction. Our very lack of purpose defeats us. We experience boredom, detachment and disillusion. Before long our body reflects this imbalance and begins to miss a beat here and there. We are out of harmony with the universe. Our contribution to Life is at a minimum.

You think the idler has no tensions? They may not be apparent to the casual observer, but he has them, just the same. Life demands that we use our time, either to seek greater insight into ourselves or to express ourselves creatively in constructive action. The person who mistakes the squirrel-cage of constant frivolous activity for self-expression is destined to build and to accumulate tensions.

WHAT HAPPENS TO OUR TENSIONS AFTER RETIREMENT?

Formerly most people looked forward eagerly to their years of retirement. In that slower moving era, life was more leisurely. There was not a constant drive toward greater accomplishment and the day of retirement did not represent such a drastic change. The average person could "let down" after thirty-five or forty years of activity without being frustrated.

For a number of years following this period the majority of people looked forward to their retirement with dread. It had become synonymous in their minds with boredom. Their dread was compounded because they also feared impaired physical health and decreased income. There is a healthy swing in the other direction now, due to the attention focussed on this important segment of our population by various groups, and the wide publicity given their findings. Yet the tensions of retirement are being experienced and anticipated by too many people.

We know a couple who are an average happily married pair.

He will retire in another year and she is already fussing about how impossible it will be "when he is around the house all the time." Her picture of the time when they are thrown in each other's company twenty-four hours a day is not a happy one.

Of course, there is something basically wrong with such a companionship. Somehow they have built separate lives for themselves, instead of growing together, both in stature as human beings and in the goals and tempo of their development. They have struck off at a tangent from that broad and pleasant highway into the sunset years which they might have traversed together. Now they find themselves, at this crucial crossroads of their lives, bored with each other. They have a feeling of inner separation that they have tried to alleviate by constant social activity. The woman, in particular, feels that now her own social round will suffer.

Contrast this with another couple. They did not marry until they were in their early fifties. As their retirement age neared, they looked forward joyously to the freedom it would give them to be together all the time. Now approaching seventy, they are radiant. They have no financial worries because of the small but dependable income from their social security, and they live within it. They make a game of their housekeeping: she does the cooking, which she loves, and he washes the dishes while she plays the piano. He vacuums; she dusts. They attend many lectures and read books which enlarge their knowledge about subjects of mutual interest which they never had time to explore while working.

What an inspiration this couple could be to those who are afraid of that retirement day! The weak spot in most of the suggestions we read for making retirement happy is that they are directed toward people who are on the brink of retirement.

A well-known insurance company, in a press release on longevity, gave as the first step toward increasing one's life expectancy: "Pick yourself a long-lived set of grandparents." This quasi-humorous statement brings a smile because, so far as we know, we do not choose our ancestors! But the genes they bequeath to us have a profound effect on our statistical chances to live long. There are things *we* can do to prevent the corroding tensions generated by boredom, lethargy and the inevitable decrease in physical stamina of our latter years. Certainly additional years do not, in themselves, guarantee any lessening of tensions. Our oldsters have theirs, too. We should not assume they are free of tension because they are physically inactive. Let's look at three areas in our living which we should start developing in early adulthood if we wish to retire gracefully.

How to Train a Hobby Horse

First there is the selection of a hobby. A hobby is an avocation you would like to engage in as a vocation, providing it were feasible. Far too many of us are square pegs trying to fit ourselves into the round holes of expediency, financial demands, family precedent and pressures and our own lack of perseverance. The corners of these square pegs which are gradually worn down so they are semi-circular are our individual and innate aptitudes, our hidden capacities, our undiscovered or unexplored talents. Many a man has stifled an urge to paint, to write, to build houses or run a newspaper in order to meet the immediate needs of establishing a home and raising a family. He turns to a more lucrative position, hoping it will be temporary.

Once on that treadmill, however, his hope of breaking the routine of work-to-eat-to-live is remote. He places family security on one side of the scale of Life, his own need for self-expression on the other, and his mind is made up for him. The years slip away and he finds himself facing the twilight era with his dearest dreams of self-fulfillment still tucked away out of sight—and nearly out of reach. They would have materialized more easily had he devoted some time to them throughout the years.

We know an insurance man who retired three years ago. As a boy he showed great promise as a violinist and while in college was active in musical circles. Contrary to the usual sequence, this man made it a habit to keep up his practice all through his business career. He "made" time to practice . . . ! He accepted every invitation to play, grateful for the incentive to keep playing and to keep learning.

As a result he is using the added leisure of his retirement to feed his soul with the great music of the masters. He gives much genuine enjoyment to his listeners. He is alert, vital, stimulating to be with; his days are rich and rewarding. If his violin had remained untouched, in its case through the years until retirement, it would have seemed a strange and foreign object. His fingers, grown stiff with disuse, would have lacked the dexterity to evoke the beautiful sounds he heard in his mind. And he would sadly put it away, no doubt thinking bitterly of the lost years, when with a little more perseverance and determination, he could have devoted his spare time to self-expression.

COMMON ¢ENTS

Our financial area certainly deserves and demands early attention. Recently I read the results of a survey of one hundred men published by one of our largest insurance companies. It covered their financial standing from birth to the age of eighty. The great majority of these men never attained a stable financial independence sufficient to see them through their later years. Only three by the age of eighty could support themselves with what they earned. A few were partially self-supporting, some relied on relatives and some were totally on public welfare.

In our chapter on business and finance we discussed financial limitation as a source of some of the severest tensions man has. A more realistic training program for our young people in the management of their finances would be very beneficial to them. Too many of our youngsters leave school with only vague ideas of our money system, how it works and how to plan their life expenditures wisely. As a nation, we are not getting our money's worth. Many young couples fall prey to the high-pressured salesman with the result that thousands of homes are filled with shoddy furniture and short-lived appliances. They lack information on how to judge quality, good workmanship and durability of the goods they purchase. Impulse buying and unrealistic standards of living account for at least a portion of the unnecessary expenditures that might have been earmarked for a retirement fund.

"A Stitch in Time . . ."

The third area that demands attention previous to retirement is our physical health. We cannot misuse or abuse the body which serves us so well, for many years, and then have it respond overnight, because we decide to start pampering it. The good treatment and reasonable care given our bodies throughout the active years will pay happy dividends in the "golden years" when freedom from pain and the ability to be active are so important to us.

A Worthwhile Contribution

I mentioned earlier the scope of the studies being made of the retirement problem by many groups. Many of our large industrial firms are assuming considerable responsibility in assisting their older employees to prepare for their retirement. One company we know begins five years before a worker's retirement date to help him approach it intelligently. Individual counseling from a trained recreation director is available to each person and is invaluable in helping him decide on a hobby. Training in that hobby and in a variety of handwork is given, along with lessons in dancing and various games. Many of these people find themselves enjoying wider social contacts with more pleasure than ever before, because of the added self-confidence such instruction gives them.

During the last year they are given extra time off, adapted to their physical abilities: perhaps at first they report for work four days a week; the next six months every other day; then during the last couple of months, possibly only a day a week. Thus they become accustomed to planning how to spend their time. This is a big improvement over the old way of working full time right up to the day of retirement, which is often such a shock to the person that he cannot adjust to it and may succumb prematurely.

Companies are spending millions of dollars on this project. They are helping take the "tire" out of retirement for thousands of people, enabling them to live out more fully "the last of life, for which the first was made."

How to Eliminate
Disagreeable People

We all differ from each other, even more than the two proverbial snowflakes. Heredity, education, tradition, environment and experience all leave their marks on our personalities and characters. You seldom find two persons who think and feel the same about any one thing, not to mention agreeing on a number of things!

When we are thoroughly convinced we are right in an opinion, we also have a feeling or an emotion about it, too. We even use the words interchangeably. We will say, "That's the way I feel about it" when what we mean is actually what we *think* about it. This is especially true in the realm of the intangibles: religion, politics, human relations. We tend to entertain considerable emotion along with our mental grasp on these subjects, but not necessarily in the same ratio. We are usually "down" on things we are not "up" on. The degree of our emotion increases conversely to the degree of our familiarity with the subject.

It follows, then, that whenever we present a suggestion or an idea that is contradictory to that already held by a person, his "feeling" will automatically enter the picture. His reaction to the new idea will show you the degree of his conviction about it, PLUS the amount of emotion connected with it. If he is a well-balanced and mature person, trained in self-control, his reaction will be courteous, calm, sensible and restrained. Even so, he is still likely to blow off a little steam if he has been pricked in a vital spot.

If he differs radically from us and is too outspoken about it, he then becomes what we are apt to call a disagreeable person. We may rationalize our reaction by saying we don't like his "know-it-all" manner or the tone of his voice. Truthfully, we would not like him in any case, because he is too articulate in his disagreement with us.

One rule of thumb will help soothe our own troubled feelings when this trouble-maker comes in sight. We must remind ourselves a disagreeable person is only one we cannot control. We do not fear or dislike people we can control. Obnoxious in-laws are such only because of the control they exert on our spouse or our affairs, which we seem powerless to counteract. If they have no influence we are eventually able to overlook their minor shortcomings, or take them in stride with no ruffled feathers.

No one likes a disagreeable person. He is quickly passed from one friend or relative to another, like a hot potato. The tensions he can create in ten minutes may take us days to eradicate.

What do we do with disagreeable, troublesome people? How can we eliminate them? Again, a question or two addressed to ourselves will help: "Was I a disagreeable person yesterday? Was there something in *my* attitude toward that new idea he came up with that made him think of me as a disagreeable person?"

Your answer to questions like these will color your next exposure to a new idea. There is no pain like the pain of a new idea. Let's be sure we haven't closed our mind to an idea that might just happen to be a good one.

Erasing Resentments Based on Personalities

Ties that bind us to past events with emotions of hurt, resentment and bitterness are subtle but tenacious. We should try to rid ourselves of them because they set up potential sensitive areas that are a threat to our peace of mind. To free the mind of these tensions, which are usually connected with some personality, I have found the following technique invaluable.

First, visualize yourself in one quick glimpse that embraces all the time from your earliest memory to the present time, *as a student.* Try to see that you have learned great and fundamental truths about the tangible and intangible world about you through your experiences. Naturally, some of these lessons have been more palatable than others. Select one of the painful ones, one that brought you much distress at the time . . . something connected with another person. Isolate a particular scene from the ones that preceded and followed it: in your mind, frame it and place it in one of the old stereopticon viewers that used to be part of the equipment of every self-respecting parlor.

Now see yourself as the leading actor in this scene, and the other person in the supporting role. Hear him (or her) say the lines that led you to speak your own lines. Try to understand that the other person's role which he was playing was a part of everything that had made him as he was . . . all the factors we have discussed which go to make up a person. It is even possible that this same scene, could he recall it, would not be of as great importance to him as it was to you. However, the consequent emotion you felt about it forms the ties that bind you to it.

Actually, you are responsible only for your own lines in this little play. Your response to what was said and done determines the ultimate effect of the scene on your life. Do you remember the old college song, "I learned about women from her"? We all learn about Love and Hate, Beauty and Unselfishness, Humor and Forgiveness, Dependability and Sacrifice . . . all the lessons of life . . . from each other.

Repeat this with every scene of your past that has caused you tension. I believe when you lay your "stereopticon slide" down you will have gained enlightenment and peace of mind. You will see more clearly that *nothing happens to you except what happens through you.*

VARIATIONS IN SENSITIVITY

Our responses to Life are determined to a considerable extent by our own highly individualized nervous mechanism. Our nervous system relays our sensed information to our brain for "processing," and this processing determines our reaction to stimuli. This makes for a wide variation in people's responses to even the same physical or mental stimuli.

For instance, it has been proven that the same color may evoke different responses in different people. What appears to be a blue dress to one may appear as aqua or turquoise to another. Obviously in a driving test this could cause some problems and quite a bit of tension for both driver and instructor, if one saw red instead of green! It can be clinically proven that some individual's pain threshold is lower than that of others. People with acute hearing may be annoyed and distracted by sounds that are all but inaudible to those around them.

By reminding ourselves that these differences exist in individuals we may avoid much needless tension for ourselves. Our irritation with those whose reactions differ from our own would be cut down if we could incline ourselves toward leniency with them and treat our differences with tolerance. But the sensitivity I want to discuss falls under another definition of the term: "easily hurt or offended."

SIGNPOSTS TO SENSITIVITY

What are some of the signs in our lives that say "This Way to Tension"? We are all likely to be subjected to a rash of minor irritations.

Let's look at the man who, on getting up, is first irritated by the failure of the milkman to leave the cream for his coffee. The paper boy, doubtless limbering up his arm for softball that night, has neatly decapitated his favorite dahlia with the morning edition.

When he arrives at the office, he finds the elevator being repaired, necessitating a walk up to the third floor. Once there, his secretary's husband phones to say she won't be in today . . . she's ill. The mail contains a cancellation of an important order. He's on the receiving end this morning, and unless he is an unusually stable and self-controlled person, he is by this time a candidate for the paddy wagon or ulcer row.

If we permit ourselves to be upset by such occurrences, we will eventually become neurotic. I want to remind you that we are all busy building up our little neuroses and that many stem from trying to escape from emotionally-colored situations and still keep our self-respect. Most of us handle the big crises very well; something within us carries us through with flying colors. "It's the little things that drive you to the rack: a man may sit upon a mountain, but he can't sit upon a tack."

MEASURING STICK FOR NEUROSIS

Want a simple, dependable test of your own neurosis? The degree of our neurosis is determined by the intensity of our reactions, the importance of the things that upset us, and the number of times we become upset. If we want to correct them, the first thing we must recognize is that our responses are chain-reactors; like Hansel and Gretel, we must try to follow the trail of breadcrumbs to their source. We must try not to confuse cause with effect, but to recognize the dual role each of them plays.

Each time we are upset, our hormone balance is affected and eventually the metabolism of our bodies. We are then noticeably less efficient in our work and less clear of thought, not to mention being harder to get along with.

I once heard Dr. David Fink say that frustration is the basis for all emotion. Feelings are not emotions. When a feeling is intensified so that we experience a resulting physical reaction, it becomes an emotion.

You may have a feeling of patriotism as you sit and think

quietly about your wonderful country, how much you love it and how much you would sacrifice for it.

But attend a military parade, watch the bright flags snapping in the breeze, see the rows of young men in uniform marching in perfect unison to the stirring strains of martial music, and you may experience the *emotion* of patriotism. Quite a different thing from the *feeling*. Your heart will beat faster and seem to swell in your breast; your blood will bound in time to the music's beat, your eyes may fill with tears. These are the physical reactions that result from the previous mental processes plus the stimuli of sight and sound and probably memory. Emotions may be "good" or "bad." The experiences in our lives that are marked by strong emotions, either joyous and constructive or negative and destructive, have a profound effect on our future reactions in similar situations. They are the ones imprinted deep in the subconscious.

When we have a negative emotional response to people, words or situations, this is a "soft spot" within us that we must mark in order to avoid the tensions that go with it. Remember: *where there is an emotional bias, there is also a mental block.*

PAY ATTENTION TO YOUR EARLY MEMORIES

Up to now we have been dealing with our own specific sensitivity to outer things in our environment that may cause us super-tension. Often our sensitivity is due to the lack of understanding of some experience in our early lives.

I recall one man who came to my office for advice. The previous Sunday he had gone for an outing with his girl friend and another couple. He told me that during the afternoon they had strolled by the court house, a site of historical importance in the area. On the lawn was a Conestoga wagon, reminiscent of the early settlers. The other man's wife said, "Oh, I have a camera in the car: I'm going to get it so we can have a picture of all of us standing in front of the wagon."

My client told me he literally froze inside: he had a horror of having his picture taken. He flatly refused to be in the picture.

No amount of coaxing moved him. He made such an issue of it that it practically spoiled the day for all of them. As a result his girl friend, of whom he was quite fond, had refused to date him again.

After much inward turmoil and trying in vain to find the answer to his unaccountable emotional response, he finally decided to seek help.

We talked about his early years, his grade and high school days. He recalled that as a boy of ten or twelve, while in that awkward stage many boys go through, he went to a family picnic. Someone took a picture of the group and when his family got one of the pictures the next week, here was this boy, his hair standing on end, his shirt unbuttoned, and his trousers baggy. When his father saw the print he razzed the boy for being so stupid as to have his picture taken "looking like a bum."

Up to this time my client had had a fair relationship with his father. From that time on they drifted apart. Now, upon taking a good look at this event and recalling the ensuing years, my client realized that he had never permitted his picture to be taken again. This realization was quite a shock to him. I knew that in view of the residue of tension and emotion he still carried, it would be impossible to reach him through reasoning.

So I suggested he sit down and write out the whole episode. After he had done this, he was to imagine that a twelve-year-old boy, whom he did not know, had come to him for help with the identical experience. He was to write out his advice to that boy. As he did this, the self-analysis gave him the insight he needed. He could see that the pain of being ridiculed as a boy was so great it triggered the fear of ever having his picture taken again. His subconscious mechanism prevented him from ever placing himself in such an unfavorable position again. With this understanding he realized that Sunday afternoon he had been reacting with the emotions of a twelve-year-old boy instead of the wisdom of an adult human being.

An interesting follow-up on this case came when the young man dropped in a few days later and proudly showed me a picture of himself—taken by the girl friend!

CARRY-OVER OF EARLY MEMORIES CAN BE DISASTROUS

Mary Jones came looking for help because she had had a great deal of difficulty in her business life. She would work herself up to a supervisory position and then lose it within a matter of weeks after being promoted. This had happened repeatedly and she was rightly concerned about it.

As she turned her thoughts backward in time and looked at her first memories, she recalled travelling with her parents in a Pullman car when she was about a year and a half old. She had a beautiful new pair of bedroom slippers. As she paraded up and down the aisle in them, she drew a lot of attention from the passengers. She thoroughly enjoyed the admiration showered on her and could remember how radiant and expressive she felt. But before long the joy and the appreciation of being admired dwindled and she began to feel very superior and cocky. She was filled with her own importance and probably started misbehaving in the effort to attract still more attention.

Now as she analyzed these feelings she began to recognize that as an adult she was still carrying out these emotions in her job. She would enter an office as a new girl, be very cooperative and pleasant, strive hard to please and to gain the admiration and friendship of her fellow workers. The boss, recognizing her superior ability, would, after a time, promote her to a supervisory job. But invariably, upon receiving the promotion she changed from a warm, friendly girl seeking to be on good terms with everyone, to a very overbearing person, flaunting her authority.

As a result the boss who had seen her good qualities now discovered he would have to dismiss her in order to maintain office harmony. The moment she saw the connection between the two experiences it was a great release to her as well as a great lesson. The last time I heard from her she was a supervisor in her department of twenty-five girls, getting along nicely and happy in her work.

PAY ATTENTION TO YOUR "SORE SPOTS"

In this area of sensitivity as a cause of tension are the people who fall under the definition of easily hurt or offended. These are the souls who always twist your innocent remark into an uncomplimentary jab at their feelings; to whom you are always remonstrating, "But I didn't mean it that way!" It is always too late. Their delicate pride or self-esteem has been damaged beyond repair and you are the culprit.

It is always well to remember that these people are looking for nourishment for their self-pity, their "martyr-complex." The moment they are successful in finding one, their tension is released—because it is transferred to you! Though these people may be soft-spoken and nonaggressive, nevertheless they should be classed among the "disagreeable persons" we have discussed. They are not only on the *qui vive* for the first sign of an assault on their ego, but they keep you in a similar state, fearful you will make an inadvertent slip.

How can you help such a person?

After one has wrongfully accused you of jabbing him, ask him a question, "Now, what you are saying in effect, is . . ." and repeat his own statements. It won't take many applications of this technique to bring about a change.

This technique will also work with people who are constantly making insinuations with no foundation in fact. After repeating their own statement, say, "In other words, this is what you are saying?"

The martyr-complexed individual can also find help through improving his own self-acceptance and self-confidence. He should be made to realize his *self-pity is only anger that has been turned inward*. If he will go back to the root of any situation involving self-pity, he will find that somewhere his timidity kept him from acting or speaking positively at the opportune time. The more he thought about it the angrier he became. Since there was no one else to blame it on, this anger was converted into self-pity.

RECOMMENDED FOR TENSIONS: LARGE DAILY DOSES OF T L C

We all fare better in an atmosphere of love. Rob a child of the normal family affection and he quickly develops anti-social attitudes and behavior patterns. Juvenile delinquency experts tell us the majority of the youngsters who get into trouble are from homes where this normal affection is lacking. The homes responsible for some of our most vexing "problem children" are of good financial status, with parents who are active in community affairs. But on investigation it is usually found that a warm, close companionship based on love between parents and children is absent.

Is the human need for constant reassurance of care and love an innate one, or is it acquired? A recent experiment by Dr. Lee Salk, clinical psychologist on the staff of City Hospital in Elmhurst, New York brings us some interesting statistics on newly born infants. Dr. Salk started with the premise that the newborn need the comfort and reassurance of being close to their mothers, for normal development and general well-being.

Since it is the common hospital practice to remove the baby from the mother and keep it in the nursery except during feeding periods, Dr. Salk devised a test for his theory. He divided the infants into two groups. One hundred and twelve of them as a control group were kept under routine hospital nursery conditions. Near the cribs of the other group of one-hundred-and-two infants was placed a sound apparatus that transmitted a recorded and authentic heartbeat sound. Both groups received exactly the same amount of milk and care. Tape recordings were kept of the crying periods of the two groups. The "heartbeat" babies cried about forty per cent of the time as against sixty per cent for the control group. Seventy per cent of those exposed to the heartbeat sound gained weight during the test period, while only thirty-three per cent of the control group gained.

Dr. Salk's theory is that the child has become used to the close proximity of the sound of the mother's heartbeat from the very earliest moment of the functioning of its sense organs. This establishes a feeling of security and well-being in the child which is conducive to its comfort and growth. It is his experience that most new mothers automatically hold their babies to their left sides, which brings their heads close to the chest wall near the heart.

Later tests with the heartbeat machine among older children suffering from insomnia have brought favorable results. One five-year-old who had always had trouble sleeping would go to sleep within fifteen minutes with the machine turned on. Dr. Salk's explanation is that removal from proximity to the mother results in a fear of losing contact with her, the only source of stability the child has known up to that time. This is a fear symptom. The child comes to be afraid of abandonment. Nothing allays this fear like the heartbeat sound, with its constant regularity. Even a puppy, whimpering with loneliness after being removed from its mother, can be soothed by simply placing an alarm clock under its blanket; the ticking reassures it.

Who are we to say that the crying and fussing of infants who are deprived of their mother's arms is not a symptom of their tensions? Certainly no one watching a baby in a severe crying spell can doubt that it is undergoing tension. In recent years there has been a revival of the old-fashioned custom of rocking babies while they are being fed. Psychologists and baby specialists are finding that infants fare better and develop faster with considerable physical contact with their families, fathers as well as mothers. Modern pediatricians are encouraging fathers to take over at least part care of the new baby, so the child can become familiar with the touch and feel of its father.

Don't We Ever "Grow Up"?

Now we come to the natural question: if babies and children react so favorably to attention and affection, may not many of our adult tensions have their root in these lacks? The answer is "Yes." There probably is not a person alive who does not yearn for expressed affection. Witness the tremendous number of household pets, particularly in childless couples' homes, and in single people's households. We are told that one of the basic human needs is for "something to love." And there is an accompanying basic need to be loved.

But it is not enough to know we are loved: we apparently need to be reassured, over and over again, like the baby. This need is greater in some people than others, depending on many factors in their background. But it can be almost as great a need as that for food and drink. A prominent psychiatrist was interviewing a highly successful executive who had made the rounds of the medical doctors seeking relief from a series of ailments for which they could find no cause. The doctor was finally able to extract from the man admission that he was literally "at the end of his rope" as he put it, because of his unfulfilled need for the expressed affection of his wife, whom he adored.

"If she would only pat me, or say just once, 'I love you' I would be so happy," he confided. But his wife had been brought up in a home where demonstrated affection was frowned upon and she found herself unable to make affectionate gestures or to speak "love words" to him. The psychiatrist, after many sessions with the wife alone, was able to point out her shortcomings and to help her overcome her deep-rooted inhibitions. She gradually was able to show her affection, which was very real, toward her husband. His symptoms disappeared, and from then on he enjoyed a healthy, normal life.

There is an experimental trend to put our mentally ill persons in an atmosphere of warm and individualized attention. Less severe cases are placed with families who help them share the normal give and take of affectionate family life. There is nearly always more improvement in these patients than in those who are subjected to the routine care of an overcrowded institution.

It is often suggested by doctors that nurses add "T L C" to their ministrations for seriously ill patients. Experience has shown the medical profession that "tender, loving care" can have a salutary effect on the patient's recovery. In sickness one's mental and physical defenses are low, and harsh, impersonal or churlish treatment by those in charge of patients is criminal and unforgivable.

The loneliness and sense of desertion experienced by many of our old people who are forced to live in "old people's homes" is augmented by the cold and impersonal treatment many of them receive.

I am thrilled when I see an old couple, maybe bent and decrepit but smiling, walking down the street hand in hand. There is something infinitely comforting about physical contact that is an expression of love and affection: it relaxes the body, it quiets the nerves, it soothes the mind. More liberal doses of T L C will often turn disagreeable people into friends . . . and it will help dissolve our own tensions!

23

Strike Your Own Balance!

Are you aware of a vague dissatisfaction with yourself and your life? Are you bored and listless, getting no "kick" out of either your job or your recreation? Do you wake up Monday mornings hating to go to work? If your answer is "Yes" to any of these questions you are one of sixty-six per cent of the nation's workers who have these feelings about themselves. Perhaps there is not a person in that sixty-six per cent who has not at some time or other wished he could lift himself out of that category and find real joy and satisfaction in living. The truth is, you need not remain a part of this statistic.

The public is almost satiated with plans, suggestions and courses designed to help them become the persons they want to be. Like the bride entering the modern supermarket, we are confused by the sheer number and complexity of our "idea shelves" and we find ourselves stymied, wondering what to "buy."

Many people succumb to the high-pressure methods of some form of suggestion guaranteed to make them become a huge success, until their self-importance is pumped up to the boiling point. But the resulting steam pressure is allowed to blow off in empty talk without being channeled constructively to turn the wheels of accomplishment.

The Dot Is You!

The circumference represents your awareness of all the areas in your livingness. The dot is YOU! All your sensations, actions and reactions originate from your sensory perceptions of the world around you, so you ARE the center of your life. If you have tension areas, survey them objectively. Recognize that to improve them, you will need to reorganize your thought patterns as efficiently as you would your business.

In order to build new habit patterns of thinking we must take a look, somewhat simplistically, at the way man's mind works. We know that every experience we have ever had is stored permanently somewhere in the ten billion cells of our brain. All the "good" things are there, but also all the past mistakes, the half-successes, the partial victories, the self-condemnations, the false or justified guilt feelings . . . all are stored in this mental reservoir.

Now, if a man does not keep his attention focused on something outside himself, his thoughts may turn inward to dwell on these pain-producing experiences . . . all the things he hates about himself. As a result, the average person will latch onto anything to keep his mind so occupied that he doesn't have time to think of them. He will watch television for hours on end. He will be more knowledgeable about sports than about his business. He may follow the horses. The kids are not immune, either: they will sniff glue, smoke pot, drug themselves with the unbearable decibels of Rock and Roll . . . anything to barricade themselves from the realities of life and their own inadequacies.

Somewhere along the way a man may turn to positive thinking and make a lot of money as a result. But unless he has paid equal attention to his mental and spiritual growth he winds up on the mud-flats of despair because inwardly he knows his life is lacking in purpose and meaning.

SELECTIVITY IS THE ANSWER!

What he needs at this point is time for contemplation: of himself, his universe and his role in it. As he grows in understanding he will inevitably come to recognize and accept the Law of Creativity that operates that universe on every level. He will then, if he is intelligent and courageous, align himself with it.

In the vegetable kingdom this Law is exemplified by the seed, the soil and the plant. Here the earth is the creative medium, indiscriminatingly producing a peach, a plum or a watermelon, depending on the programming that went into the seed.

In the animal kingdom, of which we are a part, we see these factors as the sperm, the womb and the offspring. Generally speaking, the way that sperm has been programmed determines the type of offspring, and this holds true regardless of specie: man, dog or cattle. Man, being one echelon higher than the animal, was given the power of self-conscious thought: the power of *selecting* what he will think. So he is planting the seed of his conscious thought in the creative medium of his subjective mind *every time he thinks anything* . . . which is all the time! Inevitably this neutral, non-selective "mental soil" accepts and nourishes that seed. Up comes a crop of ideas which materialize on the visible plane as a better store, a new kind of safety pin, an improved person or an atom bomb.

So we have the soil, the womb and the subjective mind of man . . . creative media which accept any seed placed in them. The earth grows weeds as prolifically as watermelons. A womb produces a mongrel as readily as a blue ribbon thoroughbred. And a mind, directed by the conscious thought of its master, man, produces a bank robber or a bank president. THE SELECTION OF "THOUGHT SEED" DETERMINES MAN'S DESTINY!

THE #1 QUESTION

It all boils down to this: "How can I program *my* thoughts so as to bring me what I really want out of life?" I am going to give you one of the best "assists" I know, right now. It is to *write out* your very own "DEFINITENESS OF PURPOSE". This will take good hard thinking on your part but I assure you it will pay off handsomely.

Your first step is to sit down and quietly contemplate your life and your feelings about it. To repeat what I said on page 189,

—if you have tension areas, survey them objectively, and be as organized about this as you are about your business, because this IS your main business here . . . making a life as well as a living.

Always use "I am . . ." not "I am going to . . ." Your subjective mind accepts "I am . . ." as fertile seed. With this process you are building important imagery now, so refine, program and change your statements to suit your particular case as you go along. Your DEFINITENESS OF PURPOSE might run something like this:

"I, (use your name) am a successful, effective and prosperous (banker, merchant, salesman, home executive). In this work I render a good service beneficial to mankind. I think clearly, I write clearly, I communicate easily and effectively with others. I am a poised, well-balanced, warm, outgoing person. I have self-respect and enjoy the respect of others. I have the stance of a good executive. I am a good husband (wife) to my spouse (name him or her). I am a good parent, a good grandparent.

I am a healthy, happy, harmonious, prosperous person. I sleep well at night. I live a well balanced inner and outer life and I enjoy each day to its fullest. I am surrounded with interesting and stimulating friends. I have a beautiful, comfortable and delightful home in which to live and entertain my wonderful friends. I am constantly aware of the Infinite Intelligence within me, the Infinite Good around me and the abundance of the universe which is mine to enjoy to the fullest. I am grateful for my long, healthy and fruitful life in which I enjoy these realities.

This is my DEFINITENESS OF PURPOSE, Father! And so it is, for it IS so!"

As you read this daily, refining and programming your "thought seed," the creative medium of your subjective mind will accept it and it knows how to bring it about. This technique can change your life.

WRITE OUT THE CHARACTERISTICS OF THE PERSON YOU WOULD LIKE TO ASSOCIATE WITH IN EACH OF THE SIX CATEGORIES

1. *The Man Who Comes to Dinner*

What kind of person would you like to have as a guest for dinner? One who grunts "Hi" half-audibly as he comes in the door, who sits down when dinner is announced, gulps his food and pays scant attention to his host? On completing his meal he gets up with no comment and goes into the living room to watch television: about ten o'clock he says, "It's time to go," and departs. Is this the kind of man you would like to have to dinner?

Or would you like to invite the man who, as he comes in the door greets everyone warmly, making it evident he is glad to be with you? At the dinner table he will carry on a stimulating conversation, sprinkling it with bits of unusual information of interest to both children and adults. He will have the thoughtfulness to compliment your wife on the meal she had prepared. After dinner, in the living room, he will draw the children into the conversation so they too feel accepted, important and liked. As a result you will feel the evening has been worthwhile. He has been an inspiration to every member of the family.

Now, write down in detail your own qualifications for a guest.

HOME: SWEET HOME?

Home is a training ground, not only for children, but for adults as well. We have often heard, "You can take the boy out of the country, but you can't take the country out of the boy." How true! Anyone entering the business, community, social or political world carries within himself the indelible marks of the home he has left.

We agree with Dr. John Schindler when he says in his book, *How to LIVE 365 Days a Year* that the home is the biggest breeder of dis-ease in the world. He is not referring to bacteria-caused disease, but to the "dis-ease" that means a real lack of ease in human relationships. Far too often this is passed on from ore generation to the next . . . "down to the third and fourth generation," as the Bible says.

What does the word "Home" signify to you? I like the idea contained in the acrostic:

H armony
O f
M ind
E xpressing

The harmonious home is the place where sound character, attractive personality and stable lives are formed. If it is less than harmonious, the word can mean:

H ard
O n
M y
E motions, which, unfortunately, describes many homes.

All this is a kind of mental staging. The next time you go out to dinner notice how well you fit into the group, how easily you are able to reduce any tensions that might be present in that home, and as a guest, how welcome you are made to feel.

2.   What Kind of Person Would You Like to Associate With Socially?

If you are a girl, would you invite to a sorority party a girl who says, "Oh, I feel funny when I'm with a whole crowd of strangers! I never know what to say!" Suppose at the party you introduce her to everyone. But she is ill at ease and efforts at conversation with her fade after the third sentence. She finally retreats to a corner chair to remain there the rest of the evening. The details of her grooming leave something to be desired. She contributes nothing to the gathering, either as a conversationalist or a listener.

Not easily discouraged, you invite another new friend to the next party. When you pick her up she is bubbling with anticipation. Her dress is in good taste; she is perfectly groomed. She is friendly and alert, doesn't wait to be introduced to people before talking with them, and has a good line of small talk. She is always the center of a little group that is enjoying her good humor. You feel your own stock has gone up for having brought her. Is this the type of person you admire? Then you must develop yourself to be that type of person.

Write your own description of your ideal social associate. You may find you have a slight remodeling job to do on yourself. If you have any talent, even a small one, polish it up and share it with the group: there's no fun in hoarding it! Practice strengthening your weak spots . . . and the best place to practice is in that training-ground where harmony of mind expresses . . . the home! Above all, be yourself! Don't imitate!

"SINCERELY YOURS,"

A white poodle went for a walk one day and met a black poodle who was new on the block. Just then another poodle, nondescript and shaggy, came along. Ignoring him, the white poodle said to the black poodle, "What is your name?" The black one said pompously, "My name is Mimi, and I spell it 'M-i-m-i!' What is your name?" The white poodle said affectedly, "My name is Fifi, and I spell it 'F-i-f-i!' " They both turned and looking down their noses at the unclipped poodle, "And what might your name be?" Unclipped tossed his nose in the air and said haughtily, "My name is Fido . . . and I spell it 'P-H-I-D-E-A-U-X!' "

We smile at the snobbishness of the poodles. But we may recognize ourselves in Fido with his ridiculous effort to meet them on their own ground. Sometimes in a weak moment when we are suffering from tensions brought on by a lack of self-confidence, we may slip too. Pretense and sham in our human relations are like the façades of buildings on a Western movie lot . . . nothing real back of them. The person who moves through his social circle, being himself, will always be at ease. People will like him for it. Emerson pointed this out when he exclaimed "What you are speaks so loudly I cannot hear what you say!"

In the early days of the Roman Empire slave runners were used to carry all types of letters and communications. These slaves were fast runners and chosen for their dependability. In those days letters were sealed with hot wax, imprinted with the master's seal. The word for wax was "cera," a word root still widely used in our own English language today. When the master had unusual trust and faith in the honesty of his runner, he would sometimes send a valuable letter to a distant friend without sealing it, writing on the outside the words "sin cera," meaning "sent without wax." This was the highest possible commendation of his slave.

Remembering the derivation of our word "sincere" makes it a kind of special word, doesn't it? You might want to put it at the head of your list of desirable traits of the person you want to associate with, socially.

3. *What Kind of Person Do You Choose to Associate With in the Mental Realm?*

A factory that operated at only ten per cent of its capacity would not be productive enough to show a profit at the end of the year. An automobile with a governor on it permitting it only ten per cent of its potential speed would be a hazard on the highway. Since we pride ourselves on our technological progress, we would not tolerate such mechanical inefficiency.

Yet the average person utilizes only about ten per cent of his brain capacity. Most of us have settled into a pretty timeworn rut in both our conversation and thoughts, and we dislike being jarred out of it and subjected to the stress of any deviation.

We become addicted to the rounds of repetition: the weekly dinner party, the monthly card or poker party, the idle chit-chat of friends who, lacking anything better to do, "just drop in." There is a saying, "Any old fish can float and dream, but it takes a real live fish to swim upstream."

We live in the most astonishing and revolutionary age in the history of the world. Our scientists have learned more about our universe in the last thirty years than in all previously recorded history of mankind. Incredible vistas are opening up to us. We stand on the threshold of breakthroughs in many areas that will make the milestones of the past look like the railroad ties you view from the rear platform of a speeding streamliner. We have learned to adjust to miracles, and accept as commonplace, achievements that exceed the wildest dreams of prophets and wise men of ages—indeed, even of our science-fiction writers!

We have working engines no larger than your fingernail that are capable of producing self-perpetuating power from fuel cells; machines that measure the space between the stars, analyze it and send their findings back to earth; cameras that photograph a beam of light that started toward our earth from a star four billion years ago. There seems no end to the wonders of our own age. We are confident of greater ones to come.

Yet we hear comparatively little discussion of such subjects in our daily conversations. Are we too ill-informed, too reticent, too fearful of criticism to bring up such conversational topics? Instead we discuss the weather at length, the baseball score, the baby's new formula and Mary's new hat. As long as we are happy itemizing the contents of yesterday's wash to our sympathetic neighbor, our experience will be bounded by a clothesline.

The person who stimulates you, presents you with the unusual, the vitalizing, to think about. He helps you stretch the muscles of your mind. As a result you are informed, lifted and inspired. Someone has said it in a different way: "The small mind talks about things; the mediocre mind talks about people. The big mind discusses ideas."

In talking about our mental ruts, I am not implying that our thinking and conversation must be constantly erudite. This would be as dull as too much froth! But most of us could stand a higher percentage of substantial "protein" in our mental diet. A grandmother we know is taking dancing lessons and just enrolled in a "speed reading course." She always wanted really to know how to dance and was never satisfied with her reading speed. So now she is becoming an expert in intricate modern dance steps and is literally charged with enthusiasm. She was inspired by the people who have raised their reading rate from the average of one-hundred-fifty to two hundred words a minute, to ten times that amount. New horizons are opening to her as she visualizes all the books she will be able to read. Her enthusiasm is contagious.

OUR EXPERIENCES ARE BOUNDED BY THE PERIMETER OF OUR THOUGHTS! AS A MAN THINKETH IN HIS HEART, SO IS HE! WHAT WE THINK ABOUT, WE BECOME!

Be brave enough to be different! Be an iconoclast! If you have found a stimulating and challenging book, share it! Invite two or three couples in to explore it with you some evening. Take turns reading aloud (that lost art!) a page or two for each person, then discuss what you have read. What you learn may not be primarily from the book: you will learn from each other. The book is only a springboard from which you all dive into the refreshing waters of new ideas.

Almost everyone responds to the lure of the unusual or the unfamiliar. Invite new people in occasionally. When you explore, you may find treasure! The individual who is really looking for ways to stimulate his mind and add to his fund of knowledge can do so at a very nominal expenditure. The excellent paperbacks, the well stocked public libraries, adult education and night school classes offered by our public schools can enrich his life and pave the way for advancement and promotion in his work.

Write out the qualities of the person who stimulates you, mentally. Then have the courage and fortitude to prepare to be that person.

4. *What Kind of Person Would You Like to Associate With in the Business World?*

The business world is made up of routine procedures and the personnel, or if you like, the personal traits of the people involved.

What kind of man would you like to take along on a business call? One who is ill at ease; who, immediately upon entering the office, reaches for the inevitable cigarette, and further shows lack of poise by drumming his fingers on the chairarm, and interrupting your conversation? One who is vaguely apologetic in his manner, and shows his lack of self-respect in careless grooming?

I'm sure you'd prefer a man who greeted your client with a smile and extended hand, who spoke up with vigor and clarity; who was at ease and composed. A man who recalled your client's name as he shook hands on leaving, and told him how glad he was to have met him. In short, one who by his actions and courtesy showed his background of training and experience. Of course, this is the type of man you would choose.

As you write down the qualifications for your ideal business associate something within will tell you which traits you are lacking. Most of us resent criticism or advice that involves changing ourselves. However, when the "little Voice within" tells us something, we know we can rely on its wisdom and follow its direction.

The business world should interest men and women alike, because leading economists tell us that the average girl of nineteen, marrying today, can look forward to working outside her home for perhaps twenty-five years! Thirty years ago two women out of a hundred were employed in positions outside the home. Today women constitute a third of the working force of our nation!

If you are a girl, what kind of girl would you like to work with? One with habits that annoy and distract, whose mind is not on her job but on a hundred outside interests? One who carries tales from one employee to another? Would you choose the inefficient girl who does not know how to take constructive criticism? Who arrives at the office decked out as for a party? Who filches from her employer by over-staying her coffee break and habitually coming in late for work? This girl would not make an ideal office associate.

But there is the girl who is the "answer to a boss' prayer"; the steady, dependable employee, whose dress is becoming but unobtrusive and who is always impeccably groomed. The girl who is always pleasant, with an even disposition, who is interested in people and shows it. She likes her boss and her company and is loyal to them.

You know what your own ideal business girl is like. Write down every trait which she possesses, and start today to make them your own.

IDENTIFY AND BECOME!

I believe that half the reason for people's dissatisfaction with their jobs (and remember, sixty-six per cent of us are in that class!) is that they have not identified themselves as true representatives of the business they work in. Their job is not the center of their attention, even during working hours. Problems connected with the business are in the boss' domain: his headache, not theirs! The bright spots in their business careers are, in the following order: pay checks; Friday afternoons; annual vacations and fringe benefits. Dullest times of their lives are: Monday mornings; four to five o'clock daily and the hours between morning coffee break, lunch and the next coffee break.

If you are the dot in the middle of this kind of a circle, use your imagination and initiative to change yourself. Whether or not you are to blame for errors and complications at work, put yourself mentally on the managerial side. Try to see not *who* is wrong, but *what* is wrong; then what can be done to fix it. You will discover that ways "good enough" for many years are not adequate any longer.

Even if you are not on the policy-making level, have the fortitude to take ideas to the man who is. If your presentation is sound and valid, he will appreciate your interest, whether your ideas work, or not. And he will have his eye on you, from then on!

Many a business promotion has come from such attitudes as these, because the old-fashioned virtues of dependability, adequate training, competence in dealing with emergencies and willingness to accept responsibility are in short supply today. The Harvard School of Business Administration made public a survey that showed that three-quarters of the people dismissed from their jobs were victims of laziness, insubordination, inability to get along with others, cheating and trouble-making, etc. Only one-fourth lost their jobs because of a lack of knowledge or skill.

In other words, the business "circles" of seventy-five per cent of those fired from their jobs were filled with lack of interest in their work, confusion, tension, and more tension! And it all emanated from that center, which in each case is the *person* himself!

So take a survey of your business self. Are pressures, within the job or within yourself, making you so tense that everyone must step softly to keep you from "blowing your top"? Are you "too big for your britches"? Do you feel you are wasting your time on this job? Perhaps you are! Perhaps you should be ready to make the change, either in your job or in yourself, that will mean promotion and success.

Make the stance of success your own. He who assumes this

stance and plays out the role, backing it up with performance, will find there is something in the universe that responds to him in kind. When he knows his goal, it will not only step aside to let him pass, but will cooperate by bringing to him the very weapons he needs.

Don't pretend to be what you are not. However, freeing yourself of fear, anxiety and lack of self-confidence encourages your creative process to get into motion.

Search for the romance and interest in your business. Use it to spark your own performance. The days when only hard work, long hours and thrift were necessary to insure a man's success are past. If hard work alone would do it, all charwomen would be millionaires! If thrift and saving alone would do it, misers would be the happiest people in the world! We bore ourselves and everyone else with our complaints about the "old grind" and groans about having to go back "to the salt mines." Every business has a history, a present and a future that should challenge your imagination. Attaining success in the business world today demands the cultivation of your talents and capacities, the application of your whole self with vigor and perseverance.

These lines by Jesse B. Rittenhouse (from *The Door of Dreams,* Houghton Mifflin Co., Boston) fit well here:

"I bargained with Life for a penny,
And Life would pay no more,
However I begged at evening
When I counted my scanty store.

"For Life is a just employer;
He gives you what you ask,
But once you have set the wages,
Why, you must bear the task.

"I worked for a menial's hire,
Only to learn, dismayed,
That any wage I had asked of Life,
Life would have paid."

What wages are you asking of Life?

GOD LOVES A PROSPEROUS MAN

The old idea, which made piety, virtue and goodness synonymous with poverty, is disappearing. Some people think it is disappearing too fast, that the pendulum is swinging too far in the other direction. They grumble no one is interested in anything but money making. We semanticists know this is an "allness" statement, and that it *can't* be more than ninety-five per cent correct! We all laugh, though sympathetically, with the character who says, "There is nothing wrong with me that $10,000 wouldn't cure!"

I have heard the Bible misquoted as saying, "Money is the root of all evil." This should be corrected, for the sentence reads, "The love of money is the root of all evil"—quite a different thing! At any rate, our civilization is based on the medium of exchange we call money, and a certain amount of it appears to be necessary for comfortable and worthwhile living.

What is the financial status of the person you like to be associated with? Would it be a man who is always on the verge of being broke? Who skims along precariously from one pay check to the next? Whose family has "chicken today and feathers tomorrow?" Who is always dodging creditors, and whose wife dreads to answer the phone or the doorbell?

This man is filled with tensions. No other single factor, aside from serious health impairment, can make a man as jittery, as irritable and short-tempered, as financial insecurity. The pressure of never having enough to go around usually breaks out sooner or later in psychosomatic ills. He will have a steady procession of ailments: colds, sinus trouble, allergies, headaches, stomach upsets that can bloom into ulcers if he does not change his situation. You do not seek association with this man.

The wise man handles his finances wisely and does not permit them to handle him. He is subjected to the high-pressure salesmen but he does not submit to their wiles. He governs his outgo in proportion to his income, and he writes the balance in black ink. He need not have a lot of money, but he is poised and controlled; his creative process has been freed to work uninhibited since he is not the slave of debts and the cruel restraints that lack and limitation impose.

If your own financial picture and his do not coincide, you are the one who must remedy the situation. Once you set your sails in the proper direction, doors will open to you and new opportunities will begin to appear. "Power flows to the focus of attention," "Seek and you shall find," "Ask and you shall receive" and "Knock and it shall be opened unto you" are not the idle pratings of a dreamer. They are sound, dependable, proven advice as you will discover once you begin to apply these principles.

Gratitude, in some strange way that is beyond our reasoning ability to fathom, keeps up the circulation of our good, to, from and through us.

5.   *What Is the Health Status of the Person You Choose to Associate With?*

I had arrived for a dental appointment. In the waiting room I listened to the conversation of three women patients. They were having a great time, talking about their illnesses and operations, though they were strangers to each other.

Finally I said, "You girls are having a wonderful time, aren't you?" They were shocked into silence. I went on, "You know, some man would certainly love to listen to all this, wouldn't he?" One finally said, "I guess we have been talking about our troubles a lot!" Another added, "We don't dare talk this way around our husbands. Women can sympathize with each other, but men just don't understand." Her remark coincided with the opinion of a famous doctor whose article I had just read: he said that if all the sympathy in the world could be eradicated, it would wipe out about eighty per cent of its ills.

The next time you hear someone talking at length about his health problems, ask yourself, "What is his motive in relating this?" Your answer should give you insight (is it self-pity, a bid for sympathy or a desire for the limelight?) and make you more aware of your own motives, the next time you indulge in this sort of chatter.

You do not voluntarily choose as a companion one who discusses his poor health constantly. You don't necessarily lack compassion for him; he is just not good company.

If only we would use as much intelligence in taking care of ourselves as a dog does. A dog will refuse food if he doesn't feel like eating, whether from illness or lack of appetite. He will lie still and give his body a chance to recuperate after an illness. But not we! The "little Voice within" can tell us what is best for our own interests. But it cannot make us heed its warnings.

How healthy is the person you choose to associate with? Does he have the vitality and energy to do the things he wants to do, to go the places he wants to go? Although we differ in many details, we tend to fall into group types. Sometimes just the recognition of our own group characteristics can help us to handle a health situation more wisely. For instance: psychologists tell us that persons who have trouble "getting going" in the mornings fall into their own special group.

ARE YOU AN "A.M." OR A "P.M." PERSON?

Doctors concur with the psychologists that people with low blood pressure tend to be slow in getting up mornings; it seems to take them a little longer to "perk." They are the P.M. people. They face the day with considerable lethargy. They have to drive themselves to go to work; they don't really feel like functioning until noon or later. But from then they are on the "up curve" and keep going until the late hours, when they fall, exhausted, into bed.

"A.M." people bound out of bed, filled with energy. They can't wait to begin the day. They are not only self-starting, but self-operating, and are highly creative during the early hours of the day. Their performance "curve" starts meandering downhill about the middle of the afternoon and may reach its "low" as early as eight or nine o'clock in the evening.

Let's say you have decided you are mostly a "P.M.", but you would like to have some "A.M." characteristics. You don't *have* to stay a "P.M.er"! Try getting up a half hour earlier, shower, dress, and go out for a brisk walk. If you feel like ambling, *don't!* Breathe deeply, swing your arms, hum or whistle a march tune and keep time with your steps. This exercise will purify your blood of its accumulated toxins. As a bonus, you will find your thinking clarified, too. When you come in you will be ready for your day.

Personally, I feel we all are in one category: that of the alive, alert, vital person with an abundance of good health and energy. See yourself in *this* category! Exactly the same kind of life flows through you as through every other human being. Decide what you will do with your share, then go and do it!

If you have had some "Overdrawn!" notices from the bank of your physical energy reserves, don't ignore them until you go into bankruptcy. Many a person with a coronary has found a richer and more rewarding life after his recovery than before his attack, simply because he took stock of himself finally and learned to live within his capabilities. Given the chance, the body has incredible powers of rebuilding itself.

We Need a "Triple Threat" Treatment!

Our bodies seem to respond almost instantly to right treatment. But we must not expect them to respond perfectly to one healing factor, to the exclusion of all others. Common sense, care and medical attention are indicated, of course. Nor should we underrate the power of our thought to operate our bodies. Nor should we ignore the tremendous importance of giving them the right "fuel"—the elements they must have to function normally. Even our doctors are sometimes amazed to see a patient who has undergone a prolonged and severe illness regain his health and vitality, when a new, constructive mental attitude is accepted.

Charging Our Physical Batteries

There was never a time when so many people were alerted to the importance of proper food intake. We have turned into a nation of bathroom-scale-watchers. We are weight-conscious, as witness the influx of liquid weight-reducers. Mr. Average Businessman can discourse with almost scientific authority on the dangers of cholesterol in the blood.

As laymen, we do not have specialized knowledge of our nutritional needs; it takes a lifetime of study to produce an expert in this line. But we can be informed as to our basic nutritional needs and then see that they are met.

There is a fascinating new facet of the effects of food on the human body. It connects specific factors, i.e., vitamin and mineral intake, with mental and emotional problems. A deficiency of these factors may be evidenced by symptoms usually considered entirely mental in origin: chronic fatigue, irritability, loss of memory, depression, anxiety, antagonistic tendencies, loss of a sense of humor. My reason for including this excursion into nutrition is that these traits all fall under the general heading of "tensions" which we are trying to release or avoid.

In this country we seldom see cases of extreme degeneration due to vitamin and mineral deficiencies any more. But many professional men share the opinion that millions of people are "border-line" cases, bearing in their bodies and personalities evidence that they have been deprived of the necessary nutritional elements. Incidentally, the needs of all people are not the same.

In many cases where these distressing symptoms were aggravated to the point of demanding professional attention, quick changes for the better have been observed with the administration of therapeutic dosages of the deficient factors.

OUR PANDEMIC COMPLAINT

One of the most common ailments is fatigue. Chronic fatigue is either the main symptom, or an accompanying symptom of other illnesses that bring many people to seek professional help. In practically every case of abnormal fatigue the patient is found to have low blood sugar.

This shows a definite imbalance in the system, a result of faulty metabolism of starches and sugar. A craving for sweets is the body's effort to raise the blood sugar level. But the intake of sweets has exactly the reverse effect and interferes still more with the establishment of normal blood sugar level. As the patient continues his normal expenditure of energy and tries to offset his fatigue by increased sweets intake, he is caught in the midst of a vicious cycle. This syndrome, or combination of symptoms, is particularly prevalent in the highly ambitious—the bright young executive who drives himself beyond the point of common sense. We see him burning the candle at both ends and sometimes in the middle, too: combining too much night life with strenuous daytime activities: often holding down two jobs.

It is not always wise to blame our negative emotions entirely on our personality shortcomings. Many faults, such as jittery nerves, unstable temper, lack of ability to make decisions, and attitudes of suspicion, may be directly attributable to a lack of the proper proportion of certain food elements in our diet. Such a lack makes itself known also through dizziness, stomach upsets, headaches, numbness of the hands and arms, general lethargy. It is significant that alcoholics show definite evidence of vitamin and mineral shortages. When these deficiencies are corrected, not only is the general health of the individual improved, but in many cases the craving for alcohol is diminished.

The B vitamins, we are told, are particularly useful in restoring balance in a great variety of conditions. Before leaving the subject of nutrition, I want to mention that Vitamin E has been found most efficacious in helping people suffering from extreme irritability and depression. It tends to lessen the tension caused by excessive nerve sensitivity.

In the psychosomatic field we suggest you read Dr. Arnold A. Hutschnecker's excellent book, *The Will to Live* (revised 1958 edition, Prentice-Hall, Inc., Englewood Cliffs, N.J.).

As you write your description of your ideally healthy companion, it will seem a simple task. That may be because it is such a basic fundamental of "the good life." Its requisites can be counted on the fingers of one hand.

Attention to the triple-threat treatment can again make life the joyous, tension-free boon it was meant to be.

24

The Science of Happiness

We have taken considerable time to examine each of five areas in our lives. If we compare them to the five points of a star, it would be a good analogy.

In a perfect star, each point is equal to each of the others; each counterbalances its neighbor and adds its contribution to the symmetry and balance of the whole.

We have considered the person we would like to be in five categories of life. But we still have another to consider. What place is left for the spiritual phase of our being? There is only one, of course: the center! Our spiritual being *is* the center of our "star." From it radiate all the vital facets of our lives. The center is a part of each point—it makes the starting place and cannot be separated from it. Without the center there would be no balanced star; only a hit-and-miss collection of triangles.

When we use the word "spiritual" we are referring to that Center within yourself. The Center that is the Source of all the inspirational thoughts and revelations that have enlightened man's mind. How do we know Truth when we meet it? Our contact with this Center enables us to recognize it and lights our faces with the dawn of understanding.

When we turn to the Center within us, it unfailingly responds, giving us what we have asked for or needed . . . comfort, ideas, inspiration. This turning to our Center we like to call our "reach for resource." We look at all prayer as just that.

Sometimes we need the inspiration of other men's God-experiences to "prime us" in our effort to look into our own Center. Many men who have talked with God have blazed a trail for us to follow. It is a good idea to keep their books and writings near us, so we may turn to them for uplift and courage.

The works of Walter Russell offer us inspiration. As he says, he cannot show anyone how to become One with his Center, but he points the way. For instance, his *Divine Iliad* is filled with passages that gleam like jewels with the light of Truth. What day could fail to bring joy that was started with such lines as these in his "Salutation to the Day"?

"I turn my eyes to the morning and purge myself in the purity of the dawn.

My soul quickeneth with the beauty of the dawn.

Today is, and will be.

Yesterday was, and has been.

My yesterday is what I made it. I see it in memory, perfect or imperfect.

My today is what I will to make it. I will to make it perfect.

I have the power to build the day or to rend the day.

The day will be of my making, either perfect or imperfect, good or bad as I choose to live it in spirit or in flesh, on the mountain-top or earthbound.

If I rend the day I build ten other days, mayhap ten times ten, to undo the rending.

If I build the day I will have lived the day to the glory of the One in the fulfillment of that part of His purpose which is mine to fulfill.

So that I may meet the day with knowledge to build the day I will look into my soul while it is yet dawn, before the morning breaketh.

These are the words with which I greet the day.

These are the words of the morning.

This is the spirit of the dawn.

*   *   *

The power of the dynamic universe is behind my thinking.
Power is mine to give by the wayside.
I will not deny to any man who asketh the power which is mine
to give.

* * *

My day shall be filled to overflowing, yet shall I not haste the day;
nor shall I waste the day.

* * *

Blessed be the new day which descendeth upon me. I greet Thee,
O day! I cross thy threshold with joy and thanksgiving."

6. *What of the Spiritual Development of the Person You Choose to Associate With?*

"Man does not live by bread alone. . . ." But we see people
who try to. They plod along, day after day, year after year, on
the food-clothing-shelter basis of an "all-bread" diet, failing to
feed their souls. Many have not opened a book in years. They
have no desire to plumb the depths of their Inner Selves. Is it
from these that you seek spiritual companions?

I daresay the person you like to associate with has a smile on
his face, a spring in his step and a twinkle in his eye. He exudes
a confidence in himself and his world that is contagious. The five
equally balanced points of his "star" spring from his spiritual
Center, and as a result he daily becomes more like the man God
expects him to be. Write out the spiritual traits of the person
you like to associate with.

WHAT IS "SOUL-FOOD"?

How does one go about feeding one's soul? A thousand books
could not hold the answers, for as the poet puts it, "There are
sermons in stones, and books in the running brooks." To the
eye that sees truly, everything in our universe is transformed into
soul-food. One may feast on a fine poem or a daily meditation.
Close association with Nature, good music or any of the arts
can be the "pause that refreshes." We must have it daily, in the
midst of our busy lives, because cultivation of the inner man is

the most satisfying thing in life. Turning to our Center to solve a scientific, business or human problem can bring a glow of self-discovery. Time spent constructively now will pay tremendous dividends. For if one believes in immortality and that we continue some activity in another dimension after leaving this one, it is reasonable to assume we will start there where we leave off here, as far as soul-growth is concerned!

WE ALL HAVE A TURNING POINT!

About two years after losing my sight I was on the verge of suicide. Life didn't seem to be worth living.

I was having trouble making up my mind, not as to "whether" but as to "how." One night while I was debating whether I would use sleeping pills or go up and jump off the roof, the "little Voice within" said, "Now, Floyd, you have talked yourself into this. How are you going to talk yourself out of it?" Instantly I realized the truth of it. The real meaning of the saying, "All the water in the seven seas will never sink a ship unless it gets inside" dawned on me. I could see that all the fear and negativity in the world can never sink a person, unless he permits those feelings to get inside him.

As a result, from that day on I began to "talk myself out of" my doldrums. This was my turning point. From then on I began to devise physical techniques for body relaxation; I replaced thought-patterns of depression, futility and apprehension with constructive, forward-looking attitudes. However, insight into my spiritual being was the prime necessity that enabled me to make good use of my resources.

I was fortunate to find much inspirational material that was particularly well-suited to my needs. I still like to use one of Dr. Robert Bitzer's meditations, "To Start Your Day Right," from his helpful book, *All Power to You,* which I quote here with his kind permission. I really believe that if you will read this meditation every morning, thoughtfully and meaningfully, for thirty days, it can change your life.

To Start Your Day Right

"I thank Thee, Father, for this New Day
With its new opportunities;
I rejoice that God-in-me will guide me
And direct my ways so that my best
Will find full expression.
Everything that I do shall prosper.
Everywhere I go I shall find
Understanding and joy;
Everyone I meet today will be strengthened and enriched.
And I shall be blessed.
This day my purpose in life shall be fulfilled."

Let's look at these lines in detail. We know it is possible to start our day with whatever attitude we wish. To fit my own needs I change the first line to "I am grateful, Father, for this new day and its new opportunities." If we start our day with gratitude we put ourselves in a frame of mind to be teachable. When we are open, responsive and receptive to our future good, we are being teachable. These attitudes are inherent in the feeling of gratitude. When we look with expectancy toward Life, new opportunities will follow.

"I rejoice that God-in-me will guide me and direct my ways . . ." are lines packed with meaning. "God-in-me" means that we have accepted *as* truth the presence IN US of whatever Deity we acknowledge. Unless you have learned to listen to and to heed this "Voice" you are out of tune with the Infinite and will remain so until you learn to listen and to heed.

When we are willing to accept this guidance so we "rejoice" in it, we have accepted its direction. The result is that the best within us will have a chance to be fully expressed. This is the highest goal toward which a man can aim. For at our best we are confident, composed, alert and dynamic, and we operate at full capacity.

"Everything that I do shall prosper." Let's think of prosperity as the finest possible harvest of everything that we sow in the realm of money, ideas, good deeds. When we get the feeling of abundance in every phase of our lives we are living in an atmosphere of opulence that frees us from limitation and allows our every talent to be expressed fully.

"Everywhere I go I shall find understanding and joy." Every man's goal! To be loved, to be accepted, to be understood, to be happy!

"Everyone I meet today will be strengthened and enriched and I shall be blessed." This implies that those we meet will be strengthened and enriched *by us,* and that thereby *we* shall be blessed. What better contribution can we make to life than to inspire another person to realize his own greatness? The moment we do this, we are also blessed. Who gets the most happiness out of giving up a seat on a crowded bus: the one who gets it, or the one who gives it? It is obviously the one who gives it. By so doing he has stimulated his finer qualities. According to the Law of Attraction, as we enlighten, the best in others is automatically reflected back to us.

"This day my purpose in life shall be fulfilled." We like to interpret this line as follows: Life is growth, and this day we will grow! Today we move constructively into Life toward the attainment of our highest goals. To avoid the tensions of confusion and frustration, start where you are with what you have, and repeat, "Father, show me the way!"

OUR FELLOW-TRAVELERS—THE STARS!

Thirty years ago only the most daring and imaginative science-fiction writer toyed with the idea that life-forms such as ours could exist on other planets.

Today it is no longer tossed aside as impossible or only remotely conceivable. It is accepted as a possible working hypothesis by many scientists. Our provable knowledge of the size of the universe staggers the imagination of the layman, and more is being discovered about its immensity each year.

To keep our perspective we should occasionally visualize our earth as it is . . . a little pear-shaped globe of matter, spinning a thousand miles an hour on its axis and at the same time whirling around our sun at seven thousand miles an hour. Our whole solar system is only a speck in the infinite vastness of space: a small part of "The Big Wheel," as astronomers call the Milky Way. It takes us two million years to make the complete circle of the Milky Way, and we know there are billions upon billions of other planets and many other galaxies lying beyond the reach of our most powerful telescopes. They say our closest star-neighbor is twenty-five trillion light years away!

If we assume that only one in one hundred planets in our own galaxy has life such as ours, there would be at least a billion planets out there with life in some form! Our minds cannot take in such magnitude: we can only stand in awe of the Power that devised and sustains such a system.

Most of the techniques in this book as aids to relaxation are based on the "ebb and flow" principle. After action, we need rest; after concentration, release of attention; after crowds, solitude; after noise, silence. We are so constructed that we find sustenance and stimulation in the element of change. We are revitalized by contrast.

Just as our physical muscles are conditioned by stretching through their normal range of motion, so we must stretch our "spiritual muscles" to keep them from sagging. When Life begins to appear dull and uninteresting, when we become bored with our daily routine, we can regain our spark by turning our attention from the macroscopic universe, which we have just glimpsed, to the microscopic.

UNIVERSE STUFF

Let's lay down the mental telescope that gave us a pinhole view of the planets and stars in outer space, and look through our mental microscope. The world of the atom is also an intriguing one. Its enormous complexity, the constant movement that goes on within challenges our intellect and confirms our faith in the Infinite Intelligence that created both atom and planet.

In a recent book dealing with the development of the atomic and nuclear bomb we read of the incredible propensity of some elements for recreating themselves. We already have several of the giant nuclear "breeder" reactors where this takes place, and more are being built. For example, when plutonium is subjected to the "slow fission" treatment, it actually replaces itself: it has the ability to create more of itself than is used up. In other words, we take a comparatively small amount of a precious element, and by applying natural laws to it we can turn it into a still greater amount of identical material.

The implications of this fact are hard to grasp because they are so far-reaching. But it seems that man has at last at his fingertips the solution to limitless power. Through the re-creation of substance by itself it is now possible to turn the wheels of the world's machinery at a fraction of the former cost: to heat and light every home and every factory; to turn the desert into a dwelling place for man, and the arctic regions into cultivated and habitable areas. Generations yet unborn will reap the benefits of the enormous expenditure of man's energy and creative thinking that has brought this age-old dream to fruition.

We have done this in the physical realm. Can we take our more precious intangibles in the realm of mind and spirit and, by application of known principles, make them reproduce themselves in kind? Can we take our present knowledge of ourselves, and by putting it to proper use, encourage it to reproduce itself in ever greater quantities? Of course we can! Like attracts like. "You do not plant thistles and expect to reap corn."

How We Build Our Own "Reactors"

We do not work alone. We all have access to the wisdom of countless lives, made available to us through the records of books, poems, revelation and inspiration of all the arts. Many are already enjoying an era of control of their thoughts and inner activities. This enables them to start with their present supply of everything that makes living a fine and meaningful adventure and use it so that it increases. Joy, expectancy, resiliency, ingenuity, creativeness . . . all are compounded daily with proper use.

We are told that once the machinery for the giant "breeder" reactors is designed, built and put in operation, a comparatively small amount of power is necessary to keep them producing. In the early years of our lives we build the machinery of the mind and soul that will determine our mental and physical processes in later years. . . . Once the general pattern is established it takes only perseverance and application to develop it.

The man who "follows his gleam" and experiences the satisfaction of doing what he is best equipped by his nature and training to do will rebuild his energy even while he is expending it. He will re-create his vitality through his activity. In the place of boredom he will have enthusiasm and an insatiable desire for still greater expression. He will neatly sidestep the mire of lethargy and indifference, and voluntarily set his feet on the stepping stones that lead onward and upward. His physical body, ever responsive to the promptings of his Inner Self, will have a marvelous capacity to renew and rebuild itself. Consequently this man's life is destined to be long and happy. Look at the men and women you know who, in their eighties and nineties, have kept their interest and curiosity alive. They have retained the characteristics of youth: its questing mind, its ability to wonder and explore.

Within each of us is an inexhaustible reservoir of spiritual atoms: ideas, inspiration, revelations and capacities. Though these atoms are more complex than physical atoms, they too act under law, so that the whole organism of man functions as a unit. What is one of our greatest blocks to living fully and completely? Our self-inflicted tensions. But as we turn our attention to our own "star" and make sure that each point of it is based on the stable center of a workable spiritual philosophy, we will be building our own "breeder" reactor for the precious elements of life. Our bonus will be the increased insight and the thrill of self-discovery that comes when we work in rhythm with the forces of the universe.

Whatever name we ascribe to the creative Power that undergirds our world we must as we mature spiritually, acknowledge its place in our daily lives. We say with the Psalmist, "It is He who hath made us, not we ourselves!" The degree to which we acknowledge and identify ourselves with It will be, in all probability, the degree of our freedom from our supertensions.

BON VOYAGE!

As children we watched for the first evening star, and when it appeared we said with utter faith, "Star light . . . star bright! First star I've seen tonight; wish I may, wish I might, have my wish come true tonight!" Then we made a silent wish.

As we shape our own "star," we will find the tone of our own prayers gradually changing. No longer will we beseech, "Oh, God, give me . . . give me!" We will say, "Father, I *know!* And I am grateful!" We will have then established a communication with the Infinite that will bring us serenity and stability and steadiness. We will possess a true creativeness that will help us build a life free of tensions.

On your journey of self-discovery, our best wishes
From the two of us to *all* of you!
God Bless You!

EPILOGUE

During the past decade we have seen a compounding of serious local, national and world problems, and with it an increase in individual tension. The present prevalent use of violence as a means of effecting social change is upsetting millions of people. The slower and more insidious cultural and social revolutions all about us have an eroding effect on the peace of mind of people everywhere.

However, because in this book we have dealt with what we consider to be the basic causes of tension in the individual, and have offered practical and effective ways of coping with them, we believe our techniques are as pertinent and relevant today as when the book was written.

The ants laboriously tug at each single grain of sand until it falls into its proper place. The Utopia of our future will not be built by artificial mass adjustments or by the imposition of laws on the populace. Only the slow steady growth of understanding, responsibility and integrity in the individual units that make up a nation can bring that Utopia into being.

Los Angeles, 1971

HOW TO RELAX IN A BUSY WORLD
WRAP-UP

RESOLVE TO RELAX. This decision is your first step. Your present tension-pattern is just a bad habit. You formed it. You can re-form it by replacing it with a better one. This will not be easy but, like any worthwhile effort, it will pay great dividends. See Chapter 8.

EXPECT TO EXPERIENCE. Develop the attitude of expectancy. Consistently see yourself as the joyous, relaxed, radiant individual you would like to be! Program yourself to be a constructive, outgoing problem-solver! See Chapter 23.

LEARN TO LIVE. Live one moment at a time, consciously aware of who you are and in full control of your own reactions. Remember! No one else can make you tense without your consent. Listen to and be guided by that infallible inner direction THIS MINUTE, and the hours and days will take care of themselves. Train yourself to function at your best — NOW! See Chapter 24.

ALWAYS BE ALERT. Frequent, deliberate relaxation will give you the clarity of thought and the vitality to be on the lookout for signs of improvement. When you see it in others, compliment them: it will help them gain emotional stability. When you observe yourself controlling your own tensions even in small ways, praise yourself! This approval will encourage your subconscious to cooperate even more. Don't try to just suppress the symptoms, but work to dissolve the inward turmoil that is responsible for the tension. See Chapters 11, 21 and 22.

X ALWAYS STANDS FOR THE UNKNOWN. Your reactions are structured by your bank of experiences. Tension, like pain, is intensely personal, and effective ways to handle *your own* hang-ups will remain an unknown factor until you explore and analyze them, yourself.

X ALSO STANDS FOR THE RELAXATION CROSS ROADS, where you are standing now. You can decide to move in either direction: back to more tension, more "blowing your top" experiences, OR forward to "keeping your cool," toward greater mastery over your own emotions. Sometimes it may be wise to turn completely away from the pressure for awhile. This is not escapism. It is a device to give you a fresh start and a new perspective.

LIFE OFFERS continuous opportunities for growth. With desire, self-knowledge and effective techniques, you can meet each situation with a light heart and the assurance of achievement. See Chapter 7.

RECOMMENDED READING

Bailes, Dr. Frederick, *Hidden Power for Human Problems* (Prentice-Hall, Inc., Englewood Cliffs, New Jersey)

————, *Your Mind Can Heal You* (Dodd, Mead & Co., New York, N.Y.)

Bitzer, Dr. Robert, *All Power to You* (Studio Press, Hollywood, California)

————, *Ye Shall Be Comforted* (for Bereavement) (7677 Sunset Boulevard, Los Angeles, California)

Blanton, Dr. Smiley, with Arthur Gordon, *Now or Never—The Promise of the Middle Years* (Prentice-Hall, Inc., Englewood Cliffs, New Jersey)

Corbett, Margaret Darst, *Help Yourself to Better Sight* (Prentice-Hall, Inc., Englewood Cliffs, New Jersey)

Dickerson, Roy E., *#201: Home Study in Social Hygiene—Guidance in Sex Education* (a six-lesson course for Parents—$2.00) (American Institute of Family Relations)

Drury, Michael, *How to Get Along with People* (Doubleday & Co., Inc.)

Gardner, John W., *Self-Renewal — The Individual and the Innovative Society* (Harper & Rowe)

Glasser, William, M.D., *Reality Therapy,* (Harper & Row, N.Y., 1965)

Holmes, Dr. Ernest, *This Thing Called Life,* and *Creative Mind and Success* (both Dodd, Mead & Co., New York, N.Y.)

Hutschnecker, Dr. Arnold A., *The Will to Live* (1958 edition, Prentice-Hall, Inc., Englewood Cliffs, New Jersey)

Maltz, Dr. Maxwell, *Psycho-Cybernetics,* (Wilshire Book Company, Hollywood, California)

Mellersh, H. E. L., *The Story of Early Man* (Viking Press, 1960, New York, N.Y.)

Rinton, Ralph and Adalin, *Man's Way: Cave to Skyscraper* (Harper & Brothers, New York, N.Y.)

Russell, Lao, *God Will Work With You But Not For You* (Swannanoa, Waynesboro, Virginia)

Smiley, Emma, *Lessons in Truth,* (Unity, Lee's Summit, Mo.)

Index